Superb practice for students with EAL!

This CGP book is packed with practice for EAL students who are 'Developing Competence' (working at English proficiency B and C).

New language structures are introduced in a clear, friendly way, with scaffolded activities to guide students in using English accurately and independently.

It doesn't stop there! We've also included free audio files so students can listen and repeat — you can find them on this page:

www.cgpbooks.co.uk/Secondary-EAL-3

CGP — still the best! ☺

Our sole aim here at CGP is to produce the highest quality books — carefully written, immaculately presented and dangerously close to being funny.

Then we work our socks off to get them out to you — at the cheapest possible prices.

About the Authors

Sally Roberts is a KS2 EAL advisor, Advanced Practitioner and teacher trainer in EAL. She currently teaches in and promotes Global Community Schools in Nottingham, engaging children and families through first languages and cultures. She studied bilingualism and DysTEFL (Dyslexia and TEFL) at Birmingham University and Lancaster University.

Greci Cristina Queiroz Taylor has 15 years' experience in EAL/EFL, having helped over 300 KS2 EAL pupils to "make rapid progress" (Ofsted Report 2017), and she now focuses on EAL in secondary schools. She has a degree in Linguistics, a Diploma in Foreign Language Teaching, a Masters degree in Applied Linguistics and ELT and a PGCE in Modern Languages from Nottingham University.

Published by CGP

Written by Sally Roberts and Greci Cristina Queiroz Taylor.

Editors:
Keith Blackhall
Emma Cleasby
Becca Lakin
Sam Norman
Rosa Roberts
Hayley Shaw
Kirsty Sweetman

Reviewers:
Lorraine Campbell
Daniel Zywno

With thanks to Heather Cowley and Megan Mooney for the proofreading.
With thanks to Laura Jakubowski for the copyright research.

Voice artists for online audio tracks: Eben O'Brien, Phoebe Mullen and Sam Norman

Acknowledgements:
Image on page 42 Winchester College/Mary Seacole Trust/Mary Evans
Laser cutting machine image on page 53 used under licence from Shutterstock.com

Includes illustrations by Sandy Gardner Artist, email sandy@sandygardner.co.uk

ISBN: 978 1 78908 914 1
Printed by Elanders Ltd, Newcastle upon Tyne.
Clipart from Corel®

Based on the classic CGP style created by Richard Parsons.

Contents

Part 1

Section 1 — Nouns

Learning when and when not to use the definite article 'the'.

Section 2 — Adjectives and Adverbs

Practising using comparatives and superlatives; practising using 'better than', 'the best', 'worse than' and 'the worst'.

Practising using adverbs of frequency; using conditional sentences with adverbs of frequency.

Section 3 — Verbs

Practising when to use the simple present; talking about routines.

Using verbs that end in 'ought' or 'aught'; using verbs that don't change spelling in their past tense form.

Practising using phrasal verbs like 'fall down'; understanding how phrasal verbs often have different meanings to the root verb.

Section 4 — Prepositions

Practising using 'in' to make adverbials of time; practising reading out years.

Practising using 'on' to make adverbials of time; practising reading out dates.

Section 5 — Reading Comprehension

Learning the difference between retrieval and inference questions; practising writing full-sentence answers.

Section 6 — Maths Language

Practising telling the time; asking and saying at what time something happens.

Part 2

```
Part 2 revisits and builds on
what has been learned in Part 1.
```

Section 7 — Nouns

Learning to identify concrete, abstract and collective nouns.

Section 8 — Adjectives and Adverbs

Practising using participial adjectives ending in '-ed' and '-ing'.

Using adverbials of place and time to describe where and when something happened.

Section 9 — Verbs

Section 10 — Prepositions

Section 11 — Reading Comprehension

Section 12 — Maths Language

Section 13 — Using a Dictionary

Section 14 — More Subject Language

Verb Table

How to Use This Book

Working with Students with EAL

- As most of the instructions will be beyond their reading level, students will need some help to use this book.

- The same types of activities are repeated though, so in time students should be able to complete many tasks independently.

- Many of the activities work well when students work in pairs or small groups, but the majority of them can be completed on their own. Encourage the students to read their work aloud.

- Involving students who have English as a native language in your teaching can be useful — these students will reinforce their English language skills when teaching non-native speakers.

Blue and Green Colour-Coding

Most of the topics in this book are presented over two pages:

The teaching points on the left-hand pages are split into blue parts and green parts.

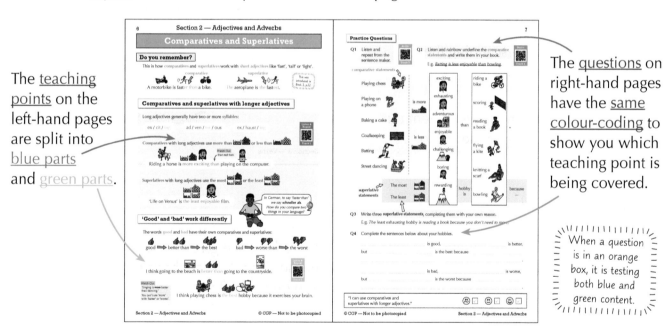

The questions on right-hand pages have the same colour-coding to show you which teaching point is being covered.

When a question is in an orange box, it is testing both blue and green content.

1) The content in blue is easier than the content in green.
2) It's a good idea to cover all the blue content first, including the activities on the right-hand page, before covering the green content.
3) With some pupils, you might choose to cover only the blue content in the first session, leaving the green content until a later date.

Students with EAL benefit from large amounts of repetition, so it's a good idea not to rush through the activities. Depending on the student's level of English, each topic may take two lessons or more to complete.

How to Use This Book

Features of the pages

Students are invited to think about the words and structures in another language.

- This demonstrates to the student that other languages are valued.

- It also promotes metacognitive thinking and links learning to ideas already familiar to the student.

The language learning begins with some grammar points and vocabulary. You should read through the explanations with the student to help them understand the grammar.

There is audio of the vocabulary and phrases on the page for students to listen to and repeat. You can access the audio tracks by scanning the QR code, or by going to:

www.cgpbooks.co.uk/Secondary-EAL-3

You may prefer to read the content out yourself, without using the audio.

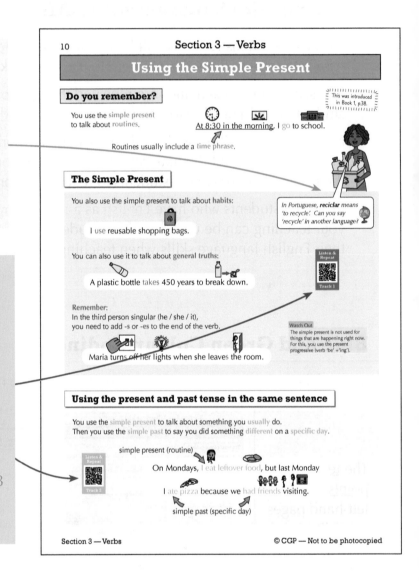

10   Section 3 — Verbs

Using the Simple Present

Do you remember?

This was introduced in Book 1, p.38.

You use the simple present to talk about routines.

At 8:30 in the morning, I go to school.

Routines usually include a time phrase.

The Simple Present

You also use the simple present to talk about habits:

I use reusable shopping bags.

You can also use it to talk about general truths:

A plastic bottle takes 450 years to break down.

In Portuguese, **reciclar** means 'to recycle'. Can you say 'recycle' in another language?

Listen & Repeat — Track 1

Remember:
In the third person singular (he / she / it), you need to add -s or -es to the end of the verb.

Maria turns off her lights when she leaves the room.

Watch Out
The simple present is not used for things that are happening right now. For this, you use the present progressive (verb 'be' +'ing').

Using the present and past tense in the same sentence

You use the simple present to talk about something you usually do. Then you use the simple past to say you did something different on a specific day.

Listen & Repeat — Track 2

simple present (routine)

On Mondays, I eat leftover food, but last Monday I ate pizza because we had friends visiting.

simple past (specific day)

Section 3 — Verbs   © CGP — Not to be photocopied

Trapdoor

1) This game needs to be played with a partner. Students are given a text which contains options for one of them to choose. The student choosing the options writes down their choices so their partner can't see.

2) The other partner reads out the text. If they say a word or phrase that their partner didn't choose, they must start reading the text again.

3) Students should keep playing until they get to the end of the text. Then they can swap roles and play again.

Rainbow Underline

1) Students will need a red, blue and green pen for this activity.

2) Students underline the words and phrases they need to make a sentence with the same coloured pen.

3) They underline one sentence in red, another in blue and another in green.

How to Use This Book

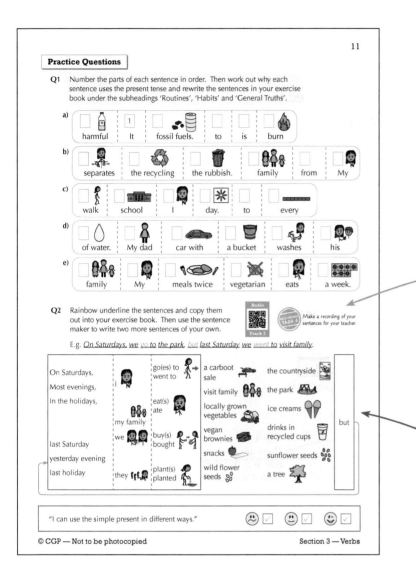

Remember and Watch Out boxes give extra tips to students. They will also point out common errors made by students with EAL.

Watch Out
You don't double the consonant if the word ends in 'y', 'w' or 'x'.

Audio recording tasks give students extra speaking practice, and allow you to monitor their progress in fluency and pronunciation. This may be particularly useful with students who are able to work independently.

Sentence makers like this are a key feature of this book. They enable students to create their own grammatical sentences independently.

To reinforce their learning, encourage students to copy out sentences into an exercise book, and then read them back to you, or to each other.

Audio Recording Tasks

1) Students will need a recording device for these activities.
2) Students read aloud phrases or sentences they have made and record them for their teacher.
3) Each recording task is labelled with a unique reference that you can ask students to use when naming their recordings.

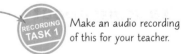

Make an audio recording of this for your teacher.

Irregular Past Tense Verbs

At the back of the book is a table showing irregular past tense verb forms.

Students can use this table as a reference when completing written work.

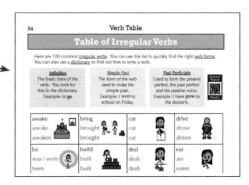

Using the Definite Article

There are some important rules to remember for <u>when to use</u> and <u>when not to use</u> 'the'.

'The' and Proper Nouns

You use the definite article **the** to talk about something specific.

the Sun   the Moon   the Queen   the London Eye

Listen & Repeat — Track 1

You shouldn't use **the** with names of:

1) **people** ⟹ ~~the~~ Anna

2) **shops** ⟹ Mum asked me to go to ~~the~~ Asda to buy some milk.

3) **cities** ⟹ At the weekend, I'm going to ~~the~~ London.

4) **languages and nationalities** ⟹ I speak ~~the~~ Spanish.

5) **countries** ⟹ I live in ~~the~~ England.

> **Watch Out**
> There are some exceptions to this rule, e.g. the Netherlands, the United States, the Philippines.

6) **continents** ⟹ Morocco is in ~~the~~ Africa.

7) **named parks and gardens** ⟹ ~~The~~ Hyde Park is near Buckingham Palace.

8) **festivals** ⟹ I got new shoes for ~~the~~ Christmas.

Talking about Something you've Already Mentioned

You also use **the** to talk about something that has already been mentioned.

Listen & Repeat — Track 2

In Lahore, there is a beautiful garden with lots of fountains and tranquil pools. The garden is called Shalimar Gardens.

In Portuguese, you usually use 'the' before names. **O Brasil é um país lindo** *means 'Brazil is a beautiful country'. Do you use the definite article in your language?*

Practice Questions

Q1 Cross out 'the' when it isn't needed and give the correct number from the list on p.4 to show the reason why. Put a tick in the box if you need 'the'. Copy out the corrected sentences in your book.

RECORDING TASK 1 — Make a recording of the corrected sentences for your teacher.

a) Last year at ~~the~~ Christmas, my family went to the London, in the England. 〔8〕〔 〕〔 〕

b) We didn't see the Queen, but we did see the Lucy, my friend, in the Hamley's toy shop. 〔✓〕〔 〕〔 〕

c) The Juan, my brother, wanted to visit the Hyde Park and the London Eye. 〔 〕〔 〕〔 〕

d) When the weather improved, I played on the pirate ship at the park in the Kensington Gardens. 〔 〕〔 〕〔 〕〔 〕

e) After the park, we listened to an audio-guide about dinosaurs in the Spanish at the Natural History Museum. 〔 〕〔 〕〔 〕

Q2 Number the parts of each sentence in the correct order.

a)
〔 〕called 〔 〕statue 〔1〕The 〔 〕is 〔 〕the Redeemer. 〔 〕Christ

〔 〕Rio de Janeiro. 〔 〕statue 〔 〕in 〔 〕There 〔 〕a 〔 〕is

b)
〔 〕garden 〔 〕very 〔1〕The 〔 〕is 〔 〕popular.

〔 〕garden 〔 〕designed 〔 〕Canada. 〔 〕a 〔 〕wonderful 〔 〕in 〔 〕Jennie Butchart

Q3 Rewrite the sentences from Q2 in the correct order in your book. Think carefully about which sentence should come first.

RECORDING TASK 2 — Make a recording of your sentences for your teacher.

"I can use the definite article 'the'." 😟✓ 🙂✓ 😉✓

Section 1 — Nouns

Comparatives and Superlatives

Do you remember?

This is how **comparatives** and **superlatives** work with **short adjectives** like 'fast', 'tall' or 'light'.

comparative

superlative

A motorbike is fast**er** than a bike.

The aeroplane is the fast**est**.

This was introduced in Book 2, p.22.

Comparatives and superlatives with longer adjectives

Long adjectives generally have two or more **syllables**:

ex / cit / ing   ad / ven / tur / ous   ex / haust / ing

Listen & Repeat
Track 1

Comparatives with long adjectives use **more than** or **less than** .

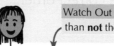

Watch Out than **not** then

Riding a horse is more exciting than playing on the computer.

Superlatives with long adjectives use **the most** or **the least** .

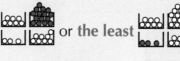

'Life on Venus' is the least enjoyable film.

*In German, to say 'faster than' we say **schneller als**. How do you compare two things in your language?*

'Good' and 'bad' work differently

The words good and bad have their own comparatives and superlatives:

good ➡ better than ➡ the best

bad ➡ worse than ➡ the worst

Listen & Repeat
Track 2

I think going to the beach is better than going to the countryside.

Watch Out
'Singing is ~~more~~ better than dancing.'
You can't use 'more' with 'better' or 'worse'.

I think playing chess is the best hobby because it exercises your brain.

Practice Questions

Q1 Listen and repeat from the sentence maker.

Track 3

Q2 Listen and rainbow underline the **comparative statements** and write them in your book.

E.g. _Batting_ _is less_ _enjoyable_ _than_ _bowling_.

Track 4

comparative statements

Playing chess

Playing on a phone

Baking a cake

Goalkeeping

Batting

Street dancing

is more

is less

exciting

exhausting

adventurous

enjoyable

challenging

boring

rewarding

than

hobby is

riding a bike

scoring

reading a book

flying a kite

knitting a scarf

bowling

because ...

superlative statements

The most

The least

Q3 Write three **superlative statements**, completing them with your own reason.

E.g. _The least exhausting hobby is reading a book because you don't need to move._

Q4 Complete the sentences below about your hobbies.

.... is good, ... is better,

but .... is the best because ....

....

.... is bad, ... is worse,

but .... is the worst because ....

....

"I can use comparatives and superlatives with longer adjectives."

Section 2 — Adjectives and Adverbs

Adverbs of Frequency

Do you remember?

You use adverbs of frequency to say how often you do things.

They come between the subject and verb.

This was introduced in Book 2, p.12.

subject

I always play cricket.

adverb of frequency   verb

Adverbs of Frequency

Adverbs of frequency tell you how often something happens.

Listen & Repeat
Track 5

always

usually

often

sometimes

rarely

almost never

never

*In Hungarian, **tüsszent** means 'to sneeze'. Can you write 'to sneeze' in another language?*

....

If I have a headache, I always have some medicine.

Conditional Sentences

Conditional sentences have a condition and a result.

A clause is a group of words that includes a subject and a verb.

If I have a cut, I sometimes put on a plaster.

condition ('if' clause)   comma   result (main clause)

Listen & Repeat
Track 6

You can change the order of the clauses. If the main clause comes first, you don't need a comma to separate the clauses.

I sometimes put on a plaster if I have a cut.

result (main clause)   condition ('if' clause)

Practice Questions

Q1 Listen and repeat from the sentence maker:

a) illnesses **b)** actions

Audio
Track 7

Audio
Track 8

You could agree actions for the illnesses and injuries in the sentence maker with a partner. Then take it in turns to call out an illness or injury, and do the action.

Q2 Listen and rainbow underline the sentences. Then write them out.

Audio
Track 9

E.g. *If I have a headache, I sometimes stay at home.*

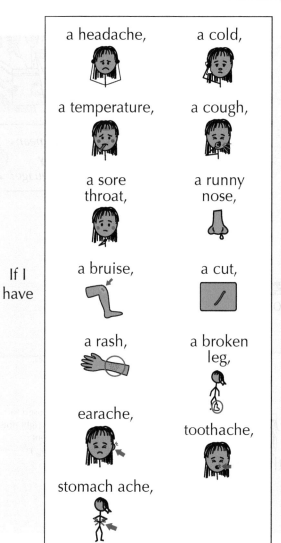

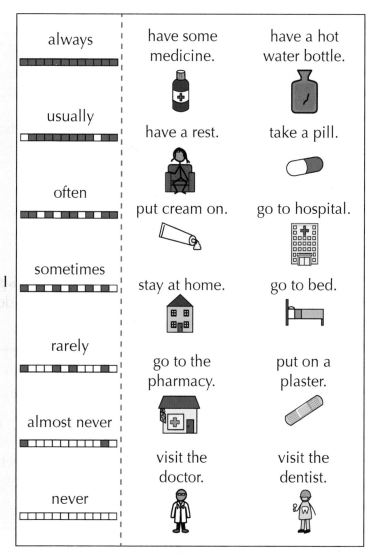

Q3 Rewrite the sentences from Q2, but swap the order of the clauses.

E.g. **If I have a cough**, I usually have some medicine.
*I usually have some medicine **if I have a cough**.*

Q4 Using the simple past tense, recount a time when you had an illness or injury, then write it in your exercise book.

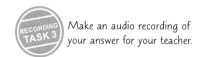
RECORDING TASK 3 — Make an audio recording of your answer for your teacher.

E.g. *Last month I had a bad cold. I had a runny nose and a sore throat. I stayed at home and went to bed. Later, I watched some television and ate ice cream. I didn't visit the doctor because I got better after 3 days.*

"I can use conditional sentences with adverbs of frequency."

Section 2 — Adjectives and Adverbs

Using the Simple Present

Do you remember?

This was introduced in Book 1, p.38.

You use the simple present to talk about routines.

At 8:30 in the morning, I go to school.

Routines usually include a time phrase.

The Simple Present

You also use the simple present to talk about **habits**:

I use reusable shopping bags.

In Portuguese, **reciclar** means 'to recycle'. Can you say 'recycle' in another language?

You can also use it to talk about **general truths**:

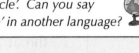

A plastic bottle takes 450 years to break down.

Listen & Repeat

Track 1

Remember:
In the third person singular (he / she / it),
you need to add **-s** or **-es** to the end of the verb.

Maria turns off her lights when she leaves the room.

Watch Out
The simple present is not used for things that are happening right now. For this, you use the present progressive (verb 'be' +'ing').

Using the present and past tense in the same sentence

You use the simple present to talk about something you usually do.
Then you use the simple past to say you did something different on a specific day.

simple present (routine)

On Mondays, I eat leftover food, but last Monday

Listen & Repeat

Track 2

I ate pizza because we had friends visiting.

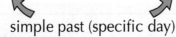

simple past (specific day)

Practice Questions

Q1 Number the parts of each sentence in order. Then work out why each sentence uses the present tense and rewrite the sentences in your exercise book under the subheadings 'Routines', 'Habits' and 'General Truths'.

a) □ harmful | 1 It | □ fossil fuels. | □ to | □ is | □ burn

b) □ separates | □ the recycling | □ the rubbish. | □ family | □ from | □ My

c) □ walk | □ school | □ I | □ day. | □ to | □ every

d) □ of water. | □ My dad | □ car with | □ a bucket | □ washes | □ his

e) □ family | □ My | □ meals twice | □ vegetarian | □ eats | □ a week.

Q2 Rainbow underline the sentences and copy them out into your exercise book. Then use the sentence maker to write two more sentences of your own.

 Audio Track 3

 RECORDING TASK 4   Make a recording of your sentences for your teacher.

E.g. *On Saturdays, we go to the park, but last Saturday we went to visit family.*

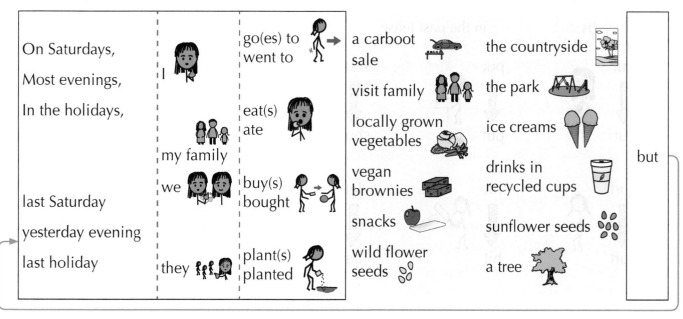

"I can use the simple present in different ways."

Section 3 — Verbs

Irregular Past Tense Verb Families

Do you remember?

This was introduced in Book 2, p.34.

Irregular verbs that follow similar patterns can be put into families.

sleep ⟹ slept

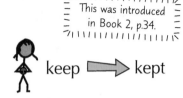

keep ⟹ kept

The -ought and -aught family

Here's another verb family — in this family, the past tense form ends with **-ought**:

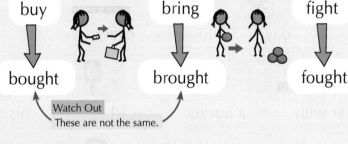

buy ⟹ bought

bring ⟹ brought

fight ⟹ fought

think ⟹ thought

Listen & Repeat Track 4

Watch Out These are not the same.

These verbs follow a similar pattern but end with **-aught** in the simple past tense.

 catch ⟹ caught

 teach ⟹ taught

In German, 'I think' is **ich denke** and 'I thought' is **ich dachte**. Can you say 'I think' and 'I thought' in another language?

....

These verbs don't change

Some verbs don't change in the past tense.

 cut ⟹ cut

put ⟹ put

shut ⟹ shut

cost ⟹ cost

 hurt ⟹ hurt

hit ⟹ hit

let ⟹ let

set ⟹ set

Listen & Repeat Track 5

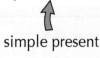 Today, I cut some paper. 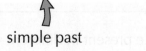 Yesterday, I cut some paper.

↑ simple present   ↑ simple past

Practice Questions

Q1 Write pairs of present and past tense sentences in your exercise book.
Use the phrases in the box below in your sentence pairs.

You could take turns to guess the simple past tense sentences while your partner acts them out.

E.g. *Today, I buy an ice cream. Yesterday, I bought an ice cream.*

> ...bring my bag to school.   ...teach my dog to jump.   ...catch a ball.
>
> ...think about my times tables.   ...fight monsters on my phone.

Q2 Write a simple past tense sentence in your exercise book
for each of these verbs that don't change from p.12.

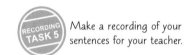
Make a recording of your sentences for your teacher.

E.g. *Last week, I cut my finger.*

cut   shut   hurt   let

put   cost   hit   set

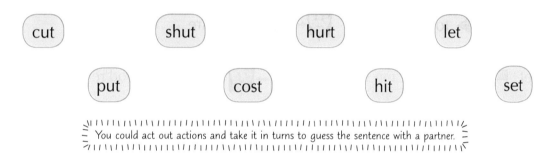
You could act out actions and take it in turns to guess the sentence with a partner.

Q3 Write the correct verb under each picture below without looking at p.12.
Then write and draw the two verbs that are missing from the family.
Cover your answers and see if you can name all 8 verbs without looking.

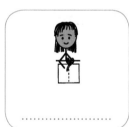

"I can use verbs that end in '-aught' and '-ought',
and verbs that don't change in the simple past."

Section 3 — Verbs

Common Phrasal Verbs

Do you remember?

A **phrasal verb** is a verb that includes an **adverb** or **preposition**.

put on   take off
preposition

This was introduced in Book 2, p.40.

The adverb or preposition changes the meaning

In **phrasal verbs**, the **adverb** or **preposition** is part of the meaning.

 fall down   pick up   line up   hurry up   go back   get out

Some **phrasal verbs** are very different from the original meaning of the verb.

to look ➡ to look up to   = to admire

to get ➡ to get along with   = to have a good relationship

to stand ➡ to stand up for   = to protect someone

Listen & Repeat

Track 6

to turn ➡ to turn to   = to ask for help

to play ➡ to play up   = to behave badly

Some verbs are followed by a **preposition** but they are **not** phrasal verbs because their **meaning is not changed**.   I swam under the water.

How do phrasal verbs change?

In the third person singular (he / she / it), only the **verb** part **changes**. The **adverb** or **preposition never changes**.

present tense (I)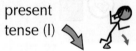
I fall over in the playground.

Listen & Repeat

Track 7

present tense (he / she / it)
Antonio falls over in the playground.

simple past tense (he / she / it)
Antonio fell over in the playground.

Practice Questions

Q1 Circle the correct phrasal verb to complete each sentence.

a) I **take off** / **pick up** my bag from the floor.

b) I **go back** / **fall down** to get my coat.

c) We **line up** / **get out** in the queue.

d) We **put on** / **hurry up** our shoes.

Q2 Use the sentence maker to write about relationships in your family in the **present** tense. Can you extend your sentences?

Some people have extra family members because a parent gets remarried. These are called step families.

E.g. *My step mum gets along with my brother when they watch football together.*

Q3 Rewrite your sentences in the simple **past** tense to talk about something that happened on a specific day in the past.

E.g. *My step mum got along with my brother when they watched football together last Saturday.*

RECORDING TASK 6 — Make a recording of your sentences for your teacher.

"I can use phrasal verbs in the present and simple past tense."

 ☑ ☑ ☑

Prepositions in Time Phrases: In

Do you remember?

Adverbials of time often have a **preposition**.
They tell us **when** something happens.

 In July, I went to the beach.

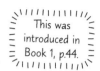 This was introduced in Book 1, p.44.

Using 'in' in adverbials of time

Like with **months**, you use the preposition **in** with **seasons**.

In London, it is cold in winter, but sometimes sunny.

London is so beautiful in May.

 Listen & Repeat — Track 1

Seasons

winter

spring

summer

autumn

You also use **in** with **different times of the day**.

In England, it is often cool in the morning and warm in the afternoon.

How to read out a year

When reading out a year as numbers, you read the
first two digits as one number and then the **second two**.

Watch Out
2000 = two thousand
2008 = two thousand and eight

2010 twenty ten   1972 nineteen seventy-two

You also use **in** with **years**.

I was born in 2010.   In 1987, a powerful storm hit the UK.

 Listen & Repeat — Track 2

Practice Questions

Audio
Track 3

Q1 Listen and repeat from the sentence maker.

Don't forget to add a full stop at the end of your sentences.

Q2 Use the sentence maker to write sentences about the weather.

E.g. *In the UK, it is usually cold in winter and warm in spring.*

RECORDING TASK 7 — Make a recording of your sentences for Q2.

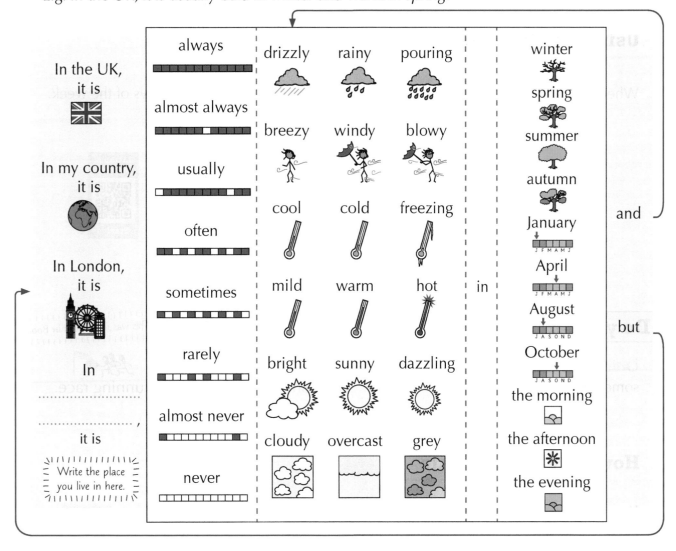

Q3 Write these years in words.
E.g. *Eighteen thirty-six*

a) 1836	**b)** 1947	**c)** 1769	**d)** 2011
e) 1912	**f)** 2018	**g)** 2000	**h)** 2007

Q4 Complete the table with the name and year of birth of you and a friend.
Then write a sentence about each person in your exercise book.

E.g. *Guru Nanak was born in 1469.*

Name	Guru Nanak	Mona Haydar		
Year Born	1469	1988		

"I can use 'in' as part of a time phrase."

Prepositions in Time Phrases: On

Do you remember?

Days of the week use the preposition **on**.

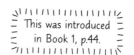

On Thursday, I made a cake.

This was introduced in Book 1, p.44.

Using 'on' in adverbials of time

When you talk about someone's routine, you use the **plural form** of the days of the week.

On Mondays, Maria has science lessons.

She needs to remember her PE kit on Wednesdays.

Listen & Repeat

Track 4

Do you remember?

Ordinal numbers tell you the **position** of something or someone in a list.

This was introduced in Book 1, p12.

Josh got 1st place in the running race.

How to read out a date

You also use **on** when you say a **date**. To say a date aloud, you need to add words that aren't written in the sentence.

My birthday is on Monday 6th March.

This is the written form.

Listen & Repeat

Track 5

This is the spoken form.

My birthday is on Monday the sixth of March.

Can you say the names of the months in another language?

Most ordinal numbers end in **-th**, except **first (1st)**, **second (2nd)**, and **third (3rd)**.

12th	21st	22nd	31st
twelfth	twenty-first	twenty-second	thirty-first

Practice Questions

Q1 Read Maria's timetable and answer the questions below.

a) What lessons does she have on Mondays? ....

b) When does she do PE? ....

	Monday	Tuesday	Wednesday	Thursday	Friday
MARCH			Spanish 1 PE Music	History 2 Art English homework	RE 3 Science Maths homework
	English 6 Science Computing	Maths 7 Geography Cooking	Spanish 8 PE Music Spanish test	History 9 Art English	RE 10 Science Maths
	English 13 Science Computing	Maths 14 Geography Cooking My birthday!	Spanish 15 PE Music	History 16 Art English	RE 17 Science Maths
	English 20 Science Computing Science project	Maths 21 Geography Cooking	Spanish 22 PE Music	History 23 Art English Art project	RE 24 Science Maths
	English 27 Science Computing	Maths 28 Geography Cooking	Spanish 29 PE Music	History 30 Art English History project	RE 31 Science Maths RE homework

Q2 Use the sentence maker to ask and answer questions about Maria's timetable.

E.g. *When do you need to remember your PE kit? I need to remember my PE kit on Wednesday.*

You could ask your friend some questions about their timetable and write about your own too.

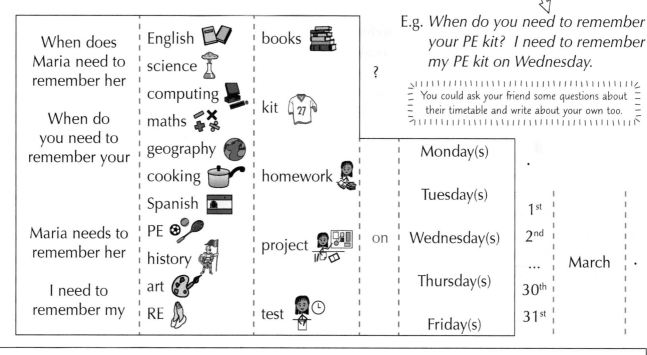

"I can use 'on' as part of a time phrase."

Section 4 — Prepositions

Retrieval and Inference

Here you will learn how to answer <u>retrieval</u> and <u>inference</u> comprehension questions.

Retrieval questions have a direct answer that you can find by reading the text.

Inference questions need a bit more thinking about
— you have to deduce (work out) the answer from the text.

> *In many cultures, children go through a ceremony to mark their move from childhood to adulthood. Does this happen in your culture?*

Practice Questions

Q1 Join the words with their definition. You can use a dictionary.

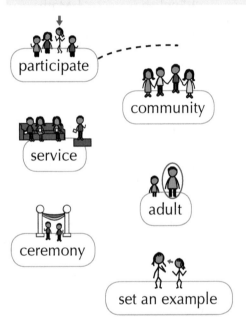

participate

community

service

adult

ceremony

set an example

a grown-up

to take part or join in

a group of people with something in common

a religious meeting

show others the right thing to do

a special religious meeting

Q2 Read and listen to the text carefully, then read the questions on the next page. Write the correct question number next to the arrow that points to the relevant part of the text.

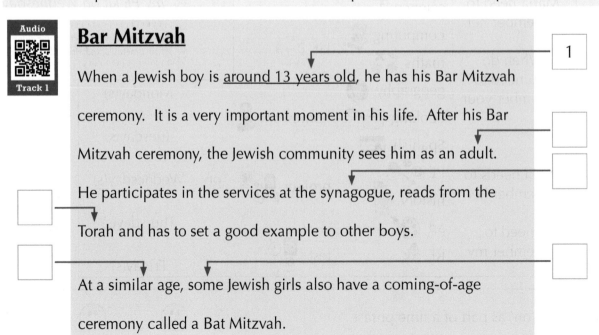

Audio Track 1

Bar Mitzvah

1

When a Jewish boy is <u>around 13 years old</u>, he has his Bar Mitzvah

ceremony. It is a very important moment in his life. After his Bar

Mitzvah ceremony, the Jewish community sees him as an adult.

He participates in the services at the synagogue, reads from the

Torah and has to set a good example to other boys.

At a similar age, some Jewish girls also have a coming-of-age

ceremony called a Bat Mitzvah.

1) How old <u>are Jewish boys when they have their Bar Mitzvah</u>? (retrieval)

2) Why <u>is it an important moment in a Jewish boy's life</u>? (inference)

3) What <u>is the Jewish holy book called</u>? (inference)

4) Where do <u>Jews hold their religious services</u>? (retrieval)

5) Do <u>all Jewish girls have a coming-of-age ceremony</u>? (retrieval)

6) How old <u>are girls when they have their Bat Mitzvah</u>? (inference)

Q3 Underline the words in the text you will need to answer each question.

Q4 Using the words you underlined in the text and the words underlined in the questions above, write a full-sentence answer to each question.

RECORDING TASK 8 Make a recording of your answers.

1) *Jewish boys are around 13 years old when they have their Bar Mitzvah.*

2)

3)

4)

5)

6)

"I can answer retrieval questions and inference questions." ☺ ☑ ☺ ☑ ☺ ☑

Section 5 — Reading Comprehension

Section 6 — Maths Language

What time is it? — 'past' the Hour

Here you will learn how to <u>tell the time</u> between '<u>o'clock</u>' and '<u>half past</u>' the hour.

What time is it?

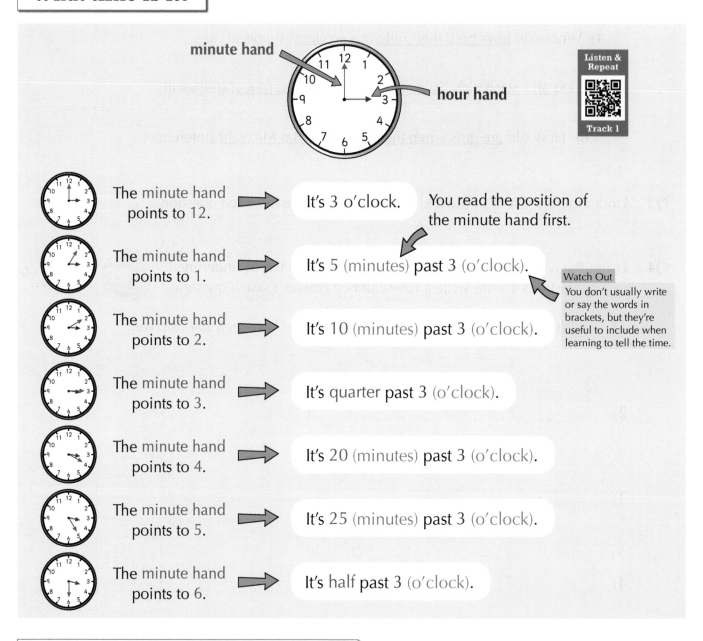

minute hand

hour hand

Listen & Repeat

Track 1

The minute hand points to 12.	It's 3 o'clock. You read the position of the minute hand first.
The minute hand points to 1.	It's 5 (minutes) past 3 (o'clock).
The minute hand points to 2.	It's 10 (minutes) past 3 (o'clock).
The minute hand points to 3.	It's quarter past 3 (o'clock).
The minute hand points to 4.	It's 20 (minutes) past 3 (o'clock).
The minute hand points to 5.	It's 25 (minutes) past 3 (o'clock).
The minute hand points to 6.	It's half past 3 (o'clock).

Watch Out
You don't usually write or say the words in brackets, but they're useful to include when learning to tell the time.

Using 'at' when telling the time

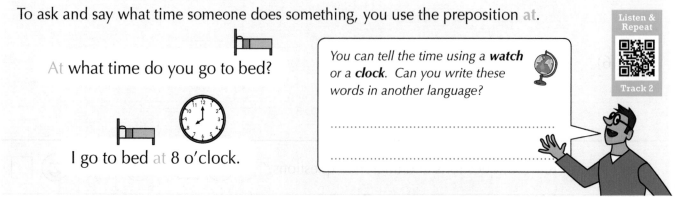

To ask and say what time someone does something, you use the preposition at.

At what time do you go to bed?

I go to bed at 8 o'clock.

*You can tell the time using a **watch** or a **clock**. Can you write these words in another language?*

....

....

Listen & Repeat

Track 2

Practice Questions

Q1 Practise counting in 5's. ➡ 5   10   15   20   25   30

Q2 Look, listen and repeat.

Q3 Write the correct letter next to each clock.

a) It's quarter past 4.

b) It's 5 past 1.

c) It's 10 past 7.

d) It's 20 past 6.

e) It's half past 10.

f) It's 25 past 12.

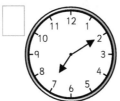  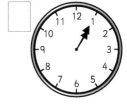

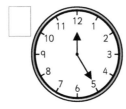  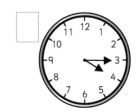

Q4 Use the time on the clocks to answer the questions below.

Remember that 3rd person verbs end in -s.

 At what time does Ali wake up?

Ali wakes up ....

....

....

....

At what time does Ali eat lunch?

 At what time does Ali go to bed?

....

....

"I can tell the time between 'o'clock' and 'half past' the hour."

Concrete, Abstract and Collective Nouns

Do you remember?

Proper nouns, such as names of people and places, start with a capital letter.

Mr Brown   China

This was introduced in Book 2, p.4.

Concrete and Abstract Nouns

Nouns which are not proper nouns are called **common nouns**.
Concrete and **abstract nouns** are both types of common nouns.

Listen & Repeat

Track 1

Concrete nouns are things you can see, hear, touch, smell or taste.

 market   food   fish    traffic jam   grass   antiques

Abstract nouns are things you **can't** see, hear, touch, smell or taste.
They are usually **ideas**, **feelings** or **emotions**.

 happiness   friendship   freedom   knowledge   frustration   patience

Felicidade, felicidad, fericire, felicità, bonheur and *Glück* all mean 'happiness' in different languages. Can you write 'happiness' in another language?

....

Collective Nouns

Collective nouns are another type of common noun.
They are used to name a group of people, animals or things.

Listen & Repeat

Track 2

a bunch of flowers

a swarm of bees

a pack of dogs

an army of soldiers

a gang of robbers

a flock of sheep

Practice Questions

Q1 Listen to the text below. Then read it to yourself. In your book, make a list of the proper nouns, the concrete nouns and the abstract nouns you can find in the text.

You could put your nouns in a table with a column for each type of noun.

Thinking of a trip to London fills me with happiness. I love to stay with

my cousin Amir. We have a wonderful friendship.

Getting stuck in traffic jams causes everyone terrible frustration, but the

London Underground gives us the freedom to choose where we would like to go.

The famous London markets are my favourite.

Traders at Billingsgate Market have a fantastic knowledge of fish. If you have an

interest in antiques you can visit Covent Garden Market, but Borough Market with all the

delicious foods is amazing.

Q2 In your exercise book, write a sentence for each of the abstract nouns on the previous page.

Make a recording of your sentences for your teacher.

E.g. *Thinking of my favourite book fills me with happiness.*
My grandparents have a fantastic knowledge of plants.

Q3 Find these collective nouns in a dictionary, then match them to the right picture.

(a litter)   (a crowd)   (a pack)   (a fleet)   (a herd)

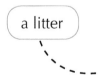

"I can tell the difference between concrete, abstract and collective nouns."

 ☑ ☑ ☑

Section 7 — Nouns

Adjectives Ending in '-ed' and 'ing'

These pages show you how to use adjectives ending in -ed and -ing correctly.

When do you use these adjectives?

Adjectives ending in **-ed** describe how a person feels.

Adjectives ending in **-ing** describe a person, thing, idea or situation.

I am...	amazed	bored	shocked	frightened	interested	annoyed
It is...	amazing	boring	shocking	frightening	interesting	annoying

I am annoyed. ➡ It is annoying.

I am annoyed because my football team lost the match.

My football team lost the match. It is so annoying!

*In Polish, **nudny** means 'boring'. Can you write **boring** in another language?*

....

How do you form these adjectives?

The adjectives below are formed by using either the past participle or present participle of a verb.

past participle	pleased	disappointed	irritated	intrigued	encouraged
present participle	pleasing	disappointing	irritating	intriguing	encouraging

I am disappointed by my favourite singer's new album.

My favourite singer's new album is disappointing.

Practice Questions

Q1 Listen and rainbow underline. Then write out the sentences in your exercise book.

Audio
Track 3

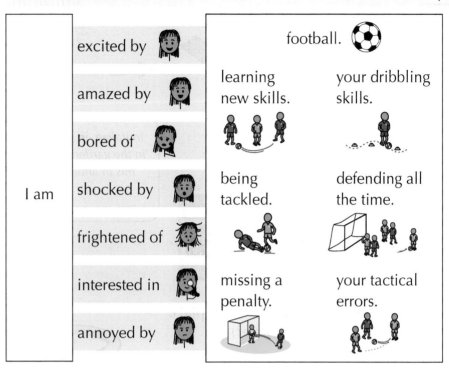

E.g. *I am excited by learning new skills.*

Q2 Use the sentence maker to write three more sentences in your exercise book.

E.g. *I am excited by football.*

Q3 Rewrite your sentences from Q2 so that they use an adjective ending in **-ing**.

E.g. *I am excited by football.* 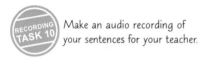 *Football is exciting.*

Q4 Use the sentence maker below to write 5 sentences.

E.g. *I am irritated by poor internet.*

RECORDING TASK 10 — Make an audio recording of your sentences for your teacher.

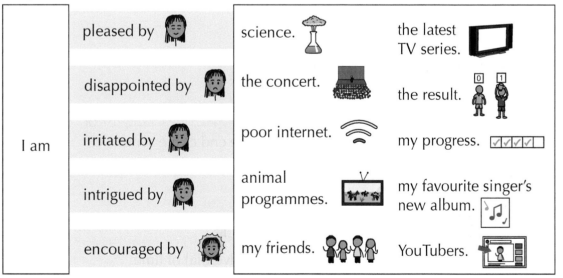

Q5 Write 3 sentences about your favourite hobbies using the adjectives ending in **-ed** and **-ing** from p.26.

E.g. *My favourite sport is tennis because it is amazing.*

"I can use adjectives ending in '-ed' and '-ing'."

Section 8 — Adjectives and Adverbs

Adverbials of Place and Time

Do you remember?

Adverbials of place show you **where** something happens.

 I swim in the swimming pool. ⟵ adverbial of place

This was introduced in Book 2, p.12.

Word Order with Adverbials of Place

The **verb** and the **object** are usually written together and the **adverbial of place** comes after the object.

*In Italian, **in giardino** means 'in the garden'. Can you write this in another language?*

....

Listen & Repeat Track 4

My dad washed the car on the driveway.

1) subject (who?) 2) verb (doing word) 3) object (what?) 4) adverbial of place (where?)

Lots of adverbials include a **preposition** (in, on, at, by, etc.).

 in an alleyway

 in the garden

 at the surgery

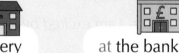 at the bank

 in a field

outside the supermarket

 at the beach

Word Order with Adverbials of Time

Adverbials of time are usually time phrases that tell you when, how long for or how often something happens. They usually come at the end of the sentence.

My dad washed the car on the driveway yesterday.

1) subject 2) verb 3) object 4) adverbial of place 5) adverbial of time (when?)

Listen & Repeat Track 5

The bus driver had a flat tyre in London twice last month.

1) subject 2) verb 3) object 4) adverbial of place 5) adverbial of time (how often?)

Practice Questions

Q1 Number the parts of each sentence in the correct order, then copy them into your book.

a)

| an alleyway. | three | 1 The policeman | in | arrested | robbers |

b)

| manager | at the | the bills | The | bank. | paid |

Q2 Underline the words to make a sentence for each person. Each sentence should include **one adverbial of place** and **one adverbial of time**. Use a different coloured pencil for each person. Copy the sentences you make into your exercise book. Remember to add a full stop.

 Record your sentences for your teacher.

E.g. *The nurse* *vaccinated* *60 people* *at the surgery* *on Saturday*.

The nurse	The mechanic	The bus driver	The superhero
the bus	a month ago	at a bus stop	at the beach
vaccinated	at 3am	stopped	60 people
a flat tyre	at the surgery	on Saturday	rescued
every 5 minutes	a child	outside the cinema	fixed

"I can use adverbials of place and time."   ✓   ✓   ✓

Section 8 — Adjectives and Adverbs

The Past Participle

This topic shows you how to write and use <u>the past participle</u> of a <u>verb</u>.

The Past Participle

The **past participle** is used in several verb forms.

> I have broken   It has broken   I had broken   It was broken

Listen & Repeat
Track 1

For **regular verbs**, the past participle is spelt the same way as the simple past form.

Today, the ants...	Yesterday, the ants...	The ants have...
pick	picked	picked
nibble	nibbled	nibbled
hatch	hatched	hatched

← past participle

The caterpillars have nibbled the plants.

↙ past participle

For **irregular verbs**, the past participle is often spelt differently.

Today, the fly...	Yesterday, the fly...	The fly has...
flies	flew	flown
goes	went	gone
eats	ate	eaten

Finding and Using the Past Participle

You can sometimes find the past participle of a verb by looking it up in a **dictionary**.

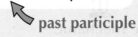

past participle ↘

hatch *v.* **hatched / hatched / hatching**
To come out of an egg.

The past participle can also be used as an **adjective**.

I was shocked when I saw so many ants in the kitchen.

↖ This **past participle** is also an **adjective**.

Listen & Repeat
Track 2

Practice Questions

Q1 Fill in the table below.

Present — Today, I...	Simple Past — Yesterday, I...	Past Participle — I have...
		flown 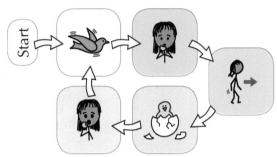
nibble		
	went	
		hatched
eat		

Q2 Play this game with a partner.

Take it in turns to roll the dice and move your counter. On each turn, say one of the forms of the verb you land on and use your pen to put a tick in the correct coloured box below. You must say all three forms of each verb to tick all the boxes. The first person to tick all their boxes wins.

Start

Player 1: ☐ ☐ ☐ ☐ ☐ ☐ ☐ ☐ ☐ ☐ ☐ ☐ ☐ ☐ ☐ ☐ ☐

Player 2: ☐ ☐ ☐ ☐ ☐ ☐ ☐ ☐ ☐ ☐ ☐ ☐ ☐ ☐ ☐ ☐ ☐

You will need two counters, two pens and a dice to play.

Q3 Complete the sentences with the correct past participle from the table above.

The worm has .... underground.

A bee has .... into the hive with its nectar.

The spider has .... the fly.

The beetle has .... from a tiny egg.

Q4 Use a dictionary to find the past participles of the verbs below. Then use them as adjectives to complete the sentences.

break: ....   **annoy:** ....

I was .... by the buzzing mosquito.

The beetle had a .... wing.

"I can form and look up past participles."   ✓

Section 9 — Verbs

The Present Perfect

In this topic, you will learn <u>when</u> and <u>how</u> to use the <u>present perfect</u>.

Using the Present Perfect

The **present perfect** talks about something that happened in the **past**.
It's mostly used when it's not important to know exactly when something happened.

Here's how you form the present perfect:

> I / you / we / they **have**
> he / she / it **has**   +   past participle

I have broken my arm.

He has grazed his knee.

You can often shorten **has** to **'s** and join it to the word before it.

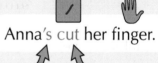

Anna's cut her finger.

has ↗   ↖ **past participle**

In a **question**:

> **Have** I / you / we / they
> **Has** he / she / it   +   past participle

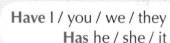

Have I broken my arm?

Has he grazed his knee?

You can shorten **have** to **'ve** and join it to the personal pronoun before it.

I've cut my finger.

have ↗   ↖ **past participle**

Other Uses of the Present Perfect

You also use the present perfect to talk about something in the **very recent past**.   ⟹    I have had my flu vaccine this morning.
↖ **present perfect**

You also use the present perfect with **for** or **since**.

 2 pm — 4 pm

She's had a headache for 2 hours.
↗ **present perfect** ↘

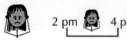

I haven't had a cold since last winter.

> *In Portuguese, **vacina** means 'vaccine'. Can you write 'vaccine' in another language?*
> ....

Practice Questions

Q1 Use the sentence maker to write some questions and answers in your exercise book.

E.g. *Have you ever cut your finger? Yes, I have cut my finger.*

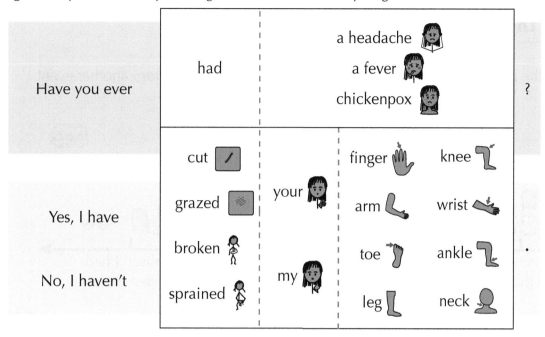

Q2 Ask a classmate or your teacher the questions you made in Q1 and write down their answers.

E.g. *Have you ever broken your arm?*
*Mrs Green **has** broken her arm.*

Remember
If you are writing about someone else:

he has...
she has...
they have...

Q3 Play a game of trapdoor. With a classmate or your teacher, take turns playing the doctor and the patient.

See p.2 for an explanation of how to play trapdoor.

Patient:	Good morning doctor.
Doctor:	Good morning, what can I do for you?
Patient:	I've **cut / burnt / broken** my **finger / toe / arm**.
Doctor:	Let me see... Okay, I can dress this and then you should visit the hospital. Is there anything else?
Patient:	Yes, I have **caught / developed / got** a terrible **cough / sore throat / headache**.
Doctor:	How long have you had it?
Patient:	I've had it **for 2 days / for a fortnight / since last week / since Tuesday**.
Doctor:	Have you taken any medicine?
Patient:	Yes. I've taken some **medicine / pills**.

Watch Out
'dress' = clean or cover an injury

"I can use the present perfect."

Section 9 — Verbs

The Past Perfect

These pages show you how to <u>form</u> and <u>use</u> the <u>past perfect</u>.

Using the Past Perfect

You use the past perfect to talk about something that happened **before** another event in the **past**. You usually use it with other tenses like the simple past.

> I put the cake in the oven, then I realised I had forgotten to add the eggs.

| forgot to add the eggs | put the cake in the oven | realised I had forgotten the eggs |

Here's how you form the past perfect:

had + past participle ➡️ I had forgotten to add the eggs.

had ↘ ↖ past participle

The Past Perfect with 'just'

You use **just** with the past perfect to talk about something that happened **only a short time before** the other event in the past.

> Dad had just mixed all the ingredients when the timer beeped.

mixed the ingredients

the timer beeped

What happened **first**?
Dad mixed all the ingredients.
What happened **last**?
The timer beeped.

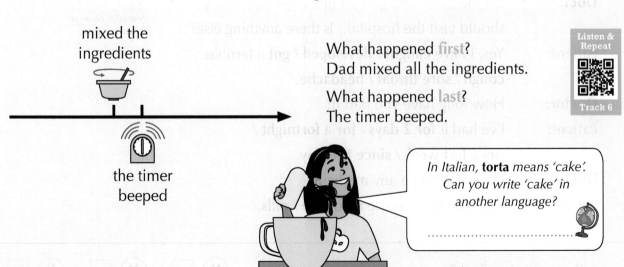

*In Italian, **torta** means 'cake'. Can you write 'cake' in another language?*

....

Practice Questions

Q1 Read the story and number the sentences in the right order.
Then rewrite the story in your exercise book and underline
the past perfect each time it is used.

[ ] I wished that I had bought a cake instead.

[ ] Back home, I put the mixture in the oven after I had mixed it.

[1] Yesterday, I decided to bake a chocolate cake for my sister.
She had eaten all the chocolate, so I went to the supermarket.

[ ] What's more, it had stuck to the tin.

[ ] Three hours later, I took my cake out of the oven.
I had forgotten to set the timer.

[ ] I hadn't written a list. When I got to the till, I realised that I'd
forgotten the chocolate, so I had to go back to get it.

[ ] It was black and it hadn't risen because I hadn't added the eggs.

Q2 Number the parts of these sentences in the right order to finish the story above.
Then write the sentences in your book. Underline the past perfect in each sentence.

a) [ ] just [ ] the [1] I [ ] had [ ] cream [ ] whipped | when my sister arrived home.

b) [ ] had [ ] cake [ ] enough, [ ] The [ ] just [ ] cooled [ ] | so I quickly covered it with the cream.

c) [ ] delicious [ ] said [ ] it [ ] She [ ] that [ ] looked [ ] | but she had just eaten lunch.

Q3 Use your own ideas to add a final sentence to the story.
Make sure you use the past perfect with 'just'.

"I can use the past perfect." 😟 ✓ 😐 ✓ 😊 ✓

The Passive Voice

In this topic, you will learn how to use the <u>passive voice</u>.

Using the Passive Voice

You use the passive voice when it's **not important to know who does something**.

> What happens in the UK on 5th November, Bonfire Night?

> A bonfire is built.   Fireworks are lit.

Listen & Repeat — Track 7

It's not important to know who builds the bonfire or lights the fireworks.

This is how you form the passive voice:

In a passive sentence, the **subject** of the sentence has something done to it.

Start the sentence with the **subject**.

Write the verb **to be** (is / are) after the subject.

A bonfire is built.

Write the **past participle** of the main verb.

verb 'to be'

Fireworks are lit.

subject

past participle of the main verb

The Passive Voice and 'by'

Do you know about any other traditional festivals? What are they called? How are they celebrated?

You can use **by** to say **who** or **what** does the action.
This information goes at the end of the sentence.

Listen & Repeat — Track 8

At the Spanish festival called 'La Tomatina',

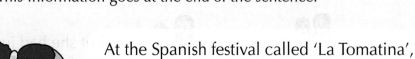
tomatoes are thrown <u>by the participants</u>.

passive voice

passive voice

Safety goggles are worn <u>by many people</u>.

Practice Questions

Q1 Number the parts of each sentence in the right order to make passive sentences.

Q2 Copy the sentences into your exercise book and underline the passive voice. Read them to your partner.

a)

| ☐ festival. | ☐ are | ☐ Naadam | 1 Mongolian horses | ☐ raced | ☐ the | ☐ at |

b)

| ☐ is | ☐ Holi | ☐ during | ☐ thrown | ☐ India. | ☐ Paint | ☐ in |

c)

| ☐ Carnival | ☐ Fancy | ☐ Brazil. | ☐ costumes | ☐ for | ☐ in | ☐ are | ☐ worn |

Q3 Rewrite these sentences so that they're in the passive voice.
The first one has been done for you.

a) Many people visit Japan during the cherry blossom festival.

During the cherry blossom festival, ...*Japan is visited by*............

many people...

RECORDING TASK 12 — Make a recording of your sentences for your teacher.

b) Taiwanese people light paper lanterns at the Lantern Festival.

At the Lantern Festival, ...

....

c) Mexican people say prayers for the dead during Day of the Dead.

During Day of the Dead, ...

....

d) Thai people throw water at Songkran.

At Songkran, ...

....

"I can use the passive voice with the present tense." ☹ ✓ ☺ ✓ ☺ ✓

Section 9 — Verbs

Using 'On', 'In' and 'At'

It can be hard to know which <u>preposition</u> to use. There are some <u>types of phrases</u> that tend to use a <u>certain preposition</u>, and there are other <u>set phrases</u> you just need to learn.

Types of Phrases that use 'on' or 'in'

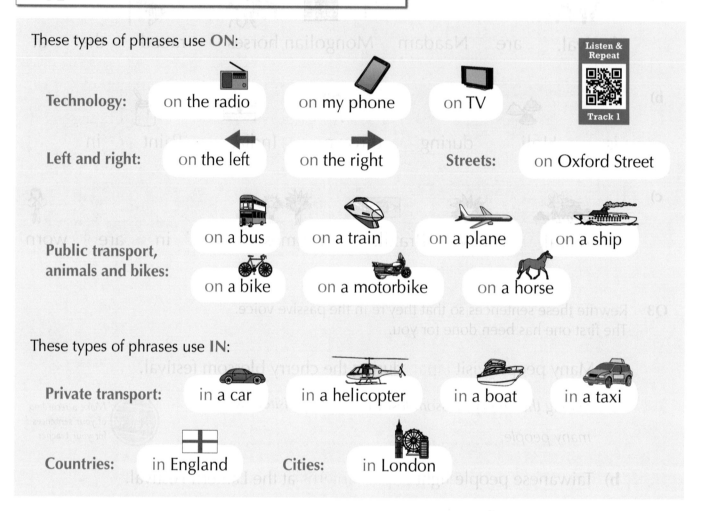

These types of phrases use **ON**:

Technology: on the radio   on my phone   on TV

Listen & Repeat Track 1

Left and right: on the left   on the right   Streets: on Oxford Street

Public transport, animals and bikes: on a bus   on a train   on a plane   on a ship   on a bike   on a motorbike   on a horse

These types of phrases use **IN**:

Private transport: in a car   in a helicopter   in a boat   in a taxi

Countries: in England   Cities: in London

Set Phrases you Have to Learn

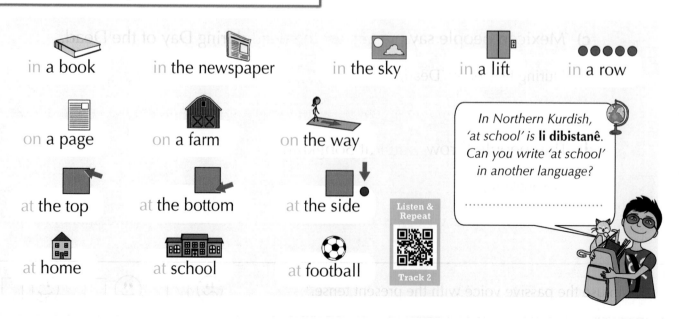

in a book   in the newspaper   in the sky   in a lift   in a row

on a page   on a farm   on the way

at the top   at the bottom   at the side

at home   at school   at football

Listen & Repeat Track 2

In Northern Kurdish, 'at school' is **li dibistanê**. Can you write 'at school' in another language?

....

Practice Questions

Q1 Use the sentence maker to make a story. Underline your choices. Make sure you use the right preposition. Read the story aloud and write it in your book.

Write the street you live on here.

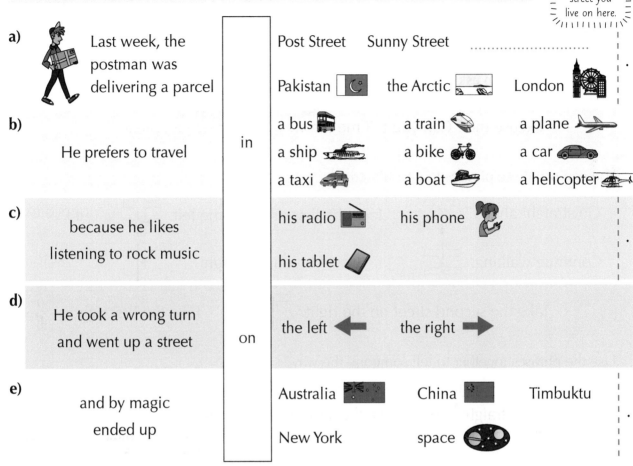

a) Last week, the postman was delivering a parcel

Post Street   Sunny Street   ....

Pakistan   the Arctic   London

b) He prefers to travel — **in**

a bus   a train   a plane
a ship   a bike   a car
a taxi   a boat   a helicopter

c) because he likes listening to rock music

his radio   his phone
his tablet

d) He took a wrong turn and went up a street — **on**

the left   the right

e) and by magic ended up

Australia   China   Timbuktu
New York   space

Q2 Write a similar story using your own ideas. Begin the story with: 'A year ago, my teacher was on holiday.'

 **RECORDING TASK 13** Make a recording of your story for your teacher.

Q3 Use the sentence maker to write 5 sentences saying where you saw something or someone.

E.g. *I saw my friends **on the way to my sister's house**.*

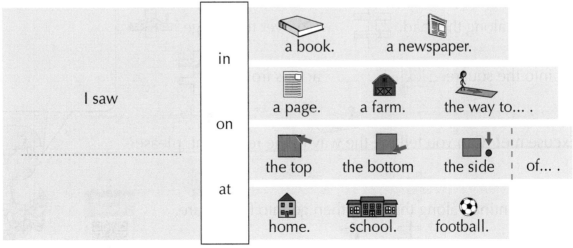

I saw ....

— in / on / at —

a book.   a newspaper.
a page.   a farm.   the way to... .
the top   the bottom   the side   of... .
home.   school.   football.

"I know when to use 'on', 'in' and 'at'."

Section 10 — Prepositions

Directions

You often use <u>prepositions</u> when <u>giving directions</u> to people.

Asking for and Giving Directions

Here's how you can **ask** for directions to somewhere:

Excuse me? Can you tell me the way to the mosque, please?

You can use these phrases to **give** directions:

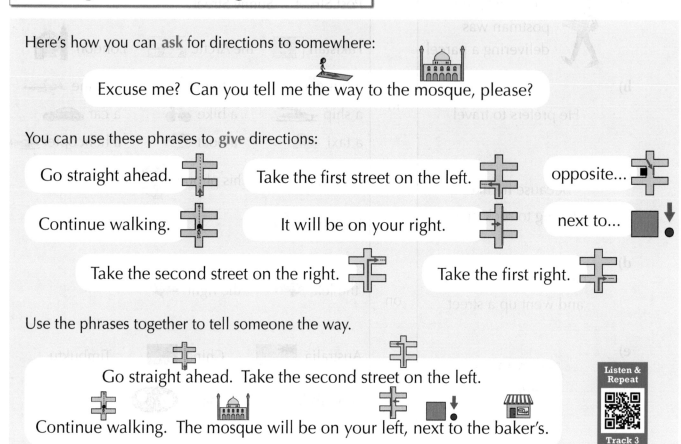

Go straight ahead.

Take the first street on the left.

opposite...

Continue walking.

It will be on your right.

next to...

Take the second street on the right.

Take the first right.

Use the phrases together to tell someone the way.

Go straight ahead. Take the second street on the left.

Continue walking. The mosque will be on your left, next to the baker's.

Listen & Repeat Track 3

More ways of Giving Directions

There are lots of other phrases you can use to give directions:

Continue along the road.   Go over the bridge.

Go into the square.   across from...

Excuse me? Can you tell me the way to the restaurant, please?

Sure! Continue along the road, then go into the square.

It will be on your left, across from the café.

In Polish, 'left' is **lewo** *and 'right' is* **prawo**. *Can you write 'left' and 'right' in another language?*

....

....

Listen & Repeat Track 4

Section 10 — Prepositions

Practice Questions

Q1 Translate the places on the map into another language in your exercise book.

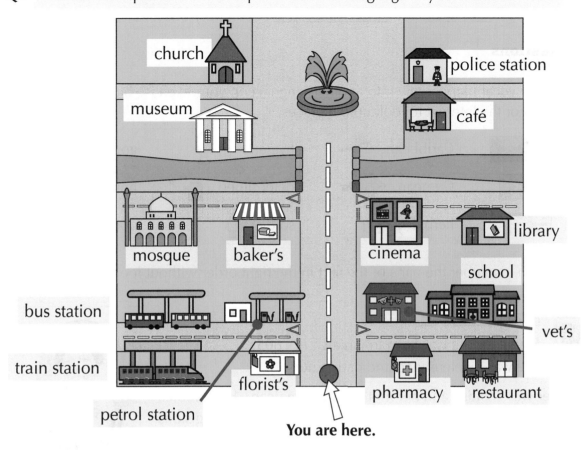

Q2 In your exercise book, write three short dialogues asking for and giving directions to places on the map. Use the dialogue text below and the map above to help you.

E.g. *Excuse me? Can you tell me the way to the vet's, please?*
Go straight ahead. Take the first road on the right. It will be on your left and next to the school. Thank you very much. Have a good day.

> Use the 'blue' text to give directions to the 'blue' places and the 'green' text to give directions to the 'green' places.

Tourist: Excuse me? Can you tell me the way to the .... , please?

Local: Go straight ahead. Take the **first / second** road on the **left / right** .

    It will be on your **left / right** and **opposite / next to** the ....

Local: Continue along the street. Go over the bridge and into the square.

    It will be on your **left / right** and **next to / across from** the ....

Tourist: Thank you very much. Have a good day.

Q3 Write directions to one of the places on a piece of paper. Write the place on the back. Can your partner or your teacher follow the directions to the correct place?

"I can ask for and give directions."

     Section 10 — Prepositions

Mary Seacole

On these pages, you'll <u>read a text</u> and <u>answer questions</u> about Mary Seacole.

Practice Questions

Q1   Translate the vocabulary below into another language in your exercise book.
Use an atlas or the Internet to look up the places.

Jamaican   Caribbean   hygiene   government

Scottish   Crimean   determined   hospital

British   herbal   soldier   poor

Q2   Read the text. Number the parts of the text in the right order without looking at the text.

Audio Track 1

Mary Seacole

Mary Seacole was born in Jamaica in 1805.
She was a determined and caring nurse.

Her father was Scottish and her mother was Jamaican. Her mother taught her about good hygiene, herbal medicines and nursing skills. Mary nursed many soldiers in the Caribbean, who were later sent to fight for the British in the Crimean War in 1853. She wanted to help the soldiers again because they were her friends, but the British government said they didn't want her help. So, Mary started her own hospital called 'The British Hotel'. The soldiers loved her. She met the famous British nurse Florence Nightingale, but they didn't work together.

When the war ended in 1856, Mary moved back to England but was very poor. Many people gave her money to say thank you for what she had done.

☐ Caribbean, who were later sent to fight for the British in the Crimean War	☐ medicines and nursing skills. Mary nursed many soldiers in the
☐ started her own hospital called 'The British Hotel'. The soldiers loved	☐ they didn't work together. When the war ended in 1856, Mary moved back to England but
☐ in 1853. She wanted to help the soldiers again because they were her	☐ was very poor. Many people gave her money to say thank you for what she had done.
☐ a determined and caring nurse. Her father was Scottish and her mother	☐ friends, but the British government said they didn't want her help. So, Mary
☐ was Jamaican. Her mother taught her about good hygiene, herbal	☐ Mary Seacole was born in Jamaica in 1805. She was
☐ her. She met the famous British nurse, Florence Nightingale, but	

Q3 Write short answers to each of these questions.

1) What <u>was Mary Seacole</u> like?

determined and caring

2) What did <u>her mother teach her</u>?

3) Why did <u>Mary want to help the soldiers</u>?

4) Why did <u>Mary start her own hospital</u>?

5) What <u>was Mary's hospital called</u>?

6) What <u>was the name of the famous British nurse that Mary met</u>?

7) Where did <u>Mary move to in 1856</u>?

Q4 Find the simple past form of these verbs that are used in the questions above.

teach: ....   start: ....

want: ....   move: ....

Q5 Use the words underlined in the questions in Q3 and your short answers to write your answers in full sentences in your exercise book.

E.g. *Mary Seacole was determined and caring.*

Remember to start your answers with the subject, then follow it with the verb in the simple past.

"I can answer reading comprehension questions."

Telling the Time — 'to' the Hour

Do you remember?

To tell the time, you read the
position of the minute hand first.

The minute
hand
points to 1.   →   It's 5 (minutes) past 3 (o'clock).

This was introduced
on p.22 of this book.

What time is it?

After the **minute hand** passes the
6 (half past), you say how long it
will be until the **next hour**.

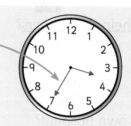

 The minute hand
points to 7.   It's 25 (minutes) to 4 (o'clock).

 The minute hand
points to 8.   It's 20 (minutes) to 4 (o'clock).

 The minute hand
points to 9.   It's quarter to 4 (o'clock).

 The minute hand
points to 10.   It's 10 (minutes) to 4 (o'clock).

 The minute hand
points to 11.   It's 5 (minutes) to 4 (o'clock).

Although the
words in brackets
aren't usually said
or written, they're
useful to include
when learning to
tell the time.

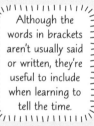
Listen &
Repeat

Track 1

Using 'at' with celebrations

You use the preposition **at** with times of celebration.

at Diwali   at Christmas   at Eid   at Halloween

Houses are decorated with small lamps
and children are given sweets at Diwali.

Listen &
Repeat

Track 2

In many countries,
children go 'Trick or
Treating' at Halloween.

*Do you have a favourite
celebration? Are there special
foods and traditions you like?*

Prepositions

Days ⇒ on
e.g. on Tuesday

Months ⇒ in
e.g. in February

Seasons ⇒ in
e.g. in summer

Years ⇒ in
e.g. in 2021

Practice Questions

Q1 Look, listen and repeat.

Q2 Write the correct letter next to each clock.

a) It's 5 to 10.

b) It's quarter to 5.

c) It's 20 to 12.

d) It's 25 to 3.

e) It's 8 o'clock.

f) It's 10 to 7.

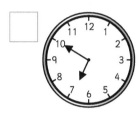  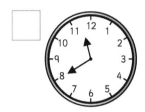

Q3 Draw hands on each clock so it matches the time below it.

a) It's 20 to 7. **b)** It's quarter to 7. **c)** It's 5 to 7. **d)** It's 7 o'clock.

Q4 Fill in the prepositions **in**, **on** and **at**. Can you spot the passive voice?

.... 2020, Eid al-Fitr was .... May, but it falls .... different months and .... different seasons because it is around 11 days earlier each year.

For most Christians, Christmas is .... 25th December. Some begin their celebrations .... midnight, with a Midnight Mass. However, many celebrate .... 6th January instead.

Time is spent with family, special meals are eaten, smart clothes are worn and gifts are given both .... Eid and .... Christmas.

"I can tell the time and use the correct preposition with time expressions."

Section 12 — Maths Language

Using a Dictionary

On these pages, you will learn how to <u>find words</u> in a <u>dictionary</u>.

How to Find a Word in a Dictionary

Words in a dictionary are in **alphabetical order**.

To find a word, you look up the first letter of the word, then the second, and so on.

When you find the word you're looking for, you'll find a
definition of the word and usually an **example** of it being used.

Audio — Track 1

fishmonger *n.*
A person or business that sells fish as a food item.

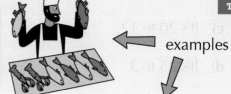

→ examples

browse *v.*
To walk around a shop looking at things without knowing what to buy.
I love to browse in bookshops.

A Dictionary tells you Other Information about the Word

A dictionary tells you if a word is...
... a **verb** (**v.**) — a doing or action word.
... a **noun** (**n.**) — a person, place or object.
... an **adjective** (**adj.**) — a word that describes a noun.
... an **adverb** (**adv.**) — a word that describes a verb or an adjective.

Audio — Track 2

A dictionary also sometimes gives you the different **forms** of a verb.

word class   past tense form   past participle   present participle

buy *v.* **bought / bought / buying**
To get something by paying money for it.

example

*Can you write **dictionary** in another language?*

....

Practice Questions

Q1 Number these shops in alphabetical order by writing a number in each box.

a) hairdresser's | supermarket | florist's | post office | greengrocer's

b) beauty salon | baker's | bookshop | barber's | bureau de change

Q2 Use a dictionary to find out what you can buy in these places.

delicatessen: *You can buy cold foods, usually cheese and meat.*

hardware shop:

butcher's:

pharmacy:

charity shop:

Q3 Use a dictionary to help you sort the words into the correct columns (some words may fit in more than one column).

purchase   busy   loudly   friendly   enquire   return

basket   till   convenient   trolley   quickly   happily   cash

noun (n.)	adjective (adj.)	verb (v.)	adverb (adv.)

Q4 Write five sentences in your book that include words from Q3.

RECORDING TASK 14 Make a recording of your sentences for your teacher.

E.g. The man behind the **till** was **friendly**.

"I can use a dictionary to find out what a word means."   ☺ ✓ ☺ ✓ ☺ ✓

Chemistry — The Periodic Table

On this page you will learn about some <u>elements</u> in the <u>periodic table</u>.

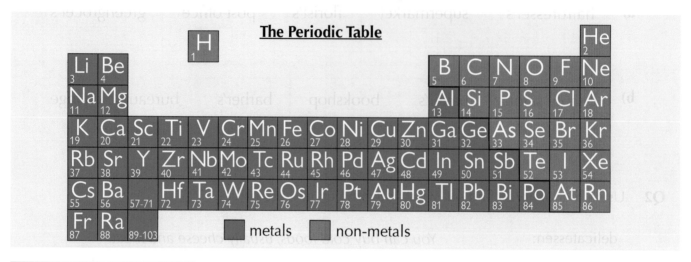

The Periodic Table

metals   non-metals

Practice Questions

Q1 Read and listen to the text below. Circle any words you don't know and translate them in your book.

Q2 Copy out the text, leaving out the underlined words. Then complete it without looking.

Everything on the planet is made of <u>atoms</u>.

Make an audio recording of the completed text for your teacher. (RECORDING TASK 15)

<u>Elements</u> are <u>pure substances</u> made of one type of atom.

 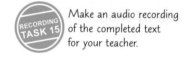

Most of the elements are <u>metals</u>. They are on the <u>left</u> of the periodic table.

Q3 Listen and repeat the sentences. Underline and translate any words that you don't know. Then choose the correct word from the box to complete each sentence.

a) The element copper (Cu) 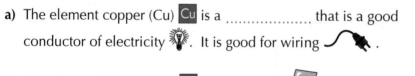 is a .... that is a good conductor of electricity 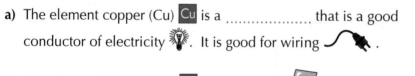. It is good for wiring 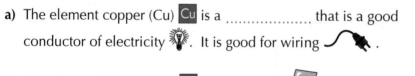 .

b) The element helium (He) He is not a metal . It is a .... used to fill balloons 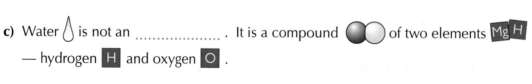 because it is lighter 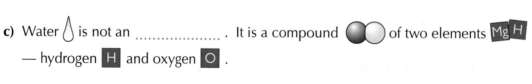 than air.

c) Water 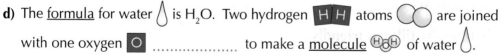 is not an .... It is a compound 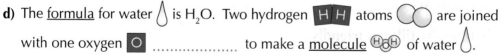 of two elements Mg H — hydrogen H and oxygen O .

d) The <u>formula</u> for water is H_2O. Two hydrogen H H atoms are joined with one oxygen O .... to make a <u>molecule</u> of water .

Audio Track 2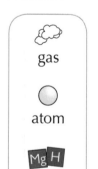

gas

atom

 element

metal

"I can talk about some elements in the periodic table."

Physics — Electricity

This page teaches you how to talk about <u>simple circuits</u>.

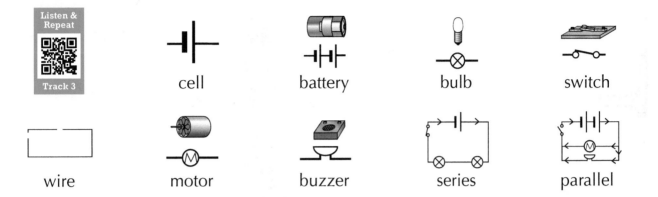

Listen & Repeat — Track 3

cell | battery | bulb | switch

wire | motor | buzzer | series | parallel

Practice Questions

Q1 Label the series circuit and the parallel circuit. You can use the pictures above to help you.

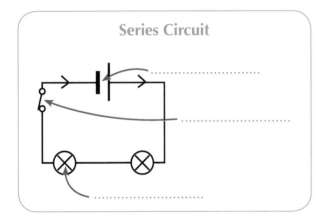

Series Circuit

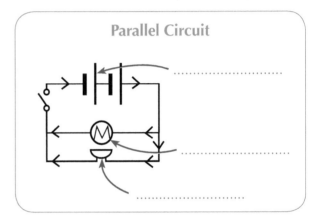

Parallel Circuit

Q2 Use the sentence maker to write two sentences about the **series circuit** in Q1.

E.g. *The bulbs will shine less brightly when there are more bulbs.*

Q3 Use the sentence maker to write two sentences about the **parallel circuit** in Q1.

E.g. *The motor will turn less quickly when there are fewer cells.*

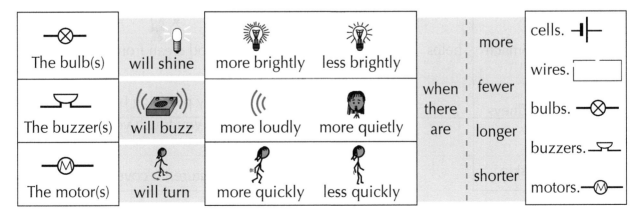

The bulb(s)	will shine	more brightly	less brightly		more	cells.
The buzzer(s)	will buzz	more loudly	more quietly	when there are	fewer	wires.
					longer	bulbs.
The motor(s)	will turn	more quickly	less quickly		shorter	buzzers.
						motors.

"I can talk about electricity."

Section 14 — More Subject Language

Biology — Human Organs

On this page you will learn about the <u>functions</u> of <u>human organs</u>.

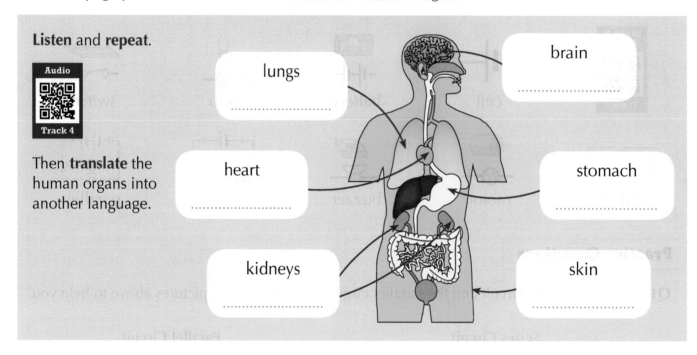

Listen and **repeat**.

Audio Track 4

Then **translate** the human organs into another language.

lungs
....

brain
....

heart
....

stomach
....

kidneys
....

skin
....

Practice Questions

Q1 Listen and rainbow underline. Write the sentences in your exercise book.
Then use the sentence maker to write about the stomach, the kidneys and the skin.

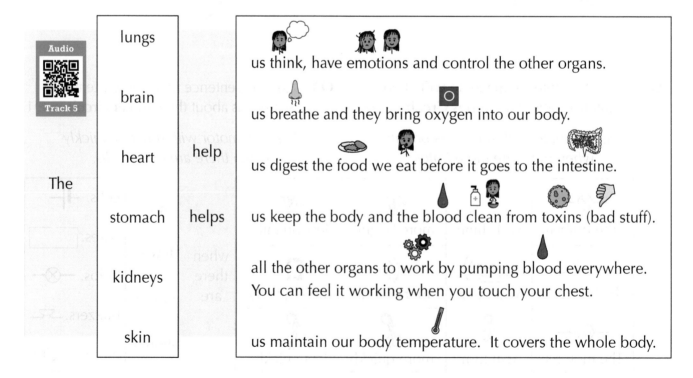

Audio Track 5

The	lungs		
	brain		us think, have emotions and control the other organs.
	heart	help	us breathe and they bring oxygen into our body.
	stomach	helps	us digest the food we eat before it goes to the intestine.
	kidneys		us keep the body and the blood clean from toxins (bad stuff).
	skin		all the other organs to work by pumping blood everywhere. You can feel it working when you touch your chest.
			us maintain our body temperature. It covers the whole body.

"I can talk about the functions of human organs."

Geography — World Climate Zones

This page teaches you how to talk about the <u>world climate zones</u> and <u>weather</u>.

Listen and **repeat**.

Audio
Track 6

Then use a dictionary to **look up** the words.

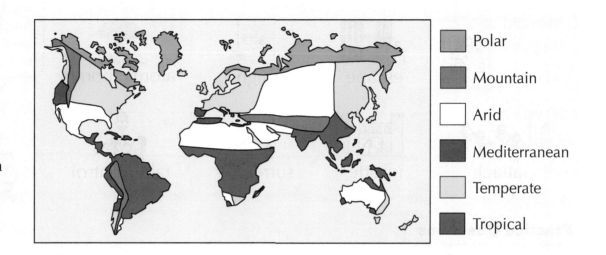

■ Polar

■ Mountain

□ Arid

■ Mediterranean

□ Temperate

■ Tropical

Practice Questions

Audio
Track 7

Q1 Listen and rainbow underline. Write the sentences in your exercise book.
Then use the sentence maker to write about arid, tropical and mountain climates.

	polar climate	Mediterranean climate		dry and hot all year.
In a			it is	usually cold with weather that changes quickly.
In an	arid climate	temperate climate		mild summers and cold winters.
A				very cold all year.
An	mountain climate	tropical climate	has	hot summers and mild winters.
				hot and wet all year.

Q2 What is the climate in the countries below? Use an atlas to help you.

a) Brazil: ....

b) UK: ....

c) Italy: ....

d) Egypt: ....

e) A country where you have lived: ....

"I can describe a country's climate."

Section 14 — More Subject Language

History — WWII Timeline

This page teaches you some of the <u>key events</u> of <u>World War Two</u>.

Listen and repeat.

Audio
Track 8

escape

sign

atomic bomb

attack

invade

surrender

take control

Can you write these words in another language? You can use a translation tool to help you.

Practice Questions

Q1 The sentences below match the dates on the timeline.
Number the words in the sentences to make them correct.

b) April — June 1940   **d)** 7th Dec 1941   **f)** 7th May 1945   **g)** August 1945

a) 1st Sept 1939   **c)** 27th Sept 1940   **e)** Sept 1943   **h)** 2nd Sept 1945

a) [ ] Poland [1] Germany [ ] began [ ] invaded [ ] WWII. [ ] which

b) [ ] many [ ] took control of [ ] including Denmark [1] Germany [ ] and France. [ ] countries

c) [ ] signed [ ] a treaty [ ] and Japan [ ] to work [1] Germany, Italy [ ] together.

d) [ ] in [ ] attacked [ ] Pearl Harbour [ ] the United States. [1] Japan

e) [ ] capture. [1] Italy [ ] surrendered [ ] Mussolini escaped [ ] but

f) [ ] surrendered [ ] Hitler's [ ] after [ ] suicide. [ ] finally [1] Germany

g) [ ] two [ ] dropped [ ] on [1] The U.S. [ ] Japan. [ ] atomic bombs

h) [ ] WWII. [ ] ended [1] Japan [ ] surrendered [ ] which

Q2 Add the correct preposition and date to start each of the sentences and copy them into your book.

Remember
On + date
In + month
Between + time + time

E.g. *On 1st September 1939, Germany invaded Poland which began WWII.*

"I know how to talk about events on a timeline." 😞 ☑ 🙂 ☑ 😉 ☑

D&T — Working with Paper

This pages teaches you how to name pieces of <u>equipment</u> used with <u>paper</u> in your <u>D&T lessons</u>.

Listen and **repeat**.

Audio
Track 9

Then **translate** the words into another language.

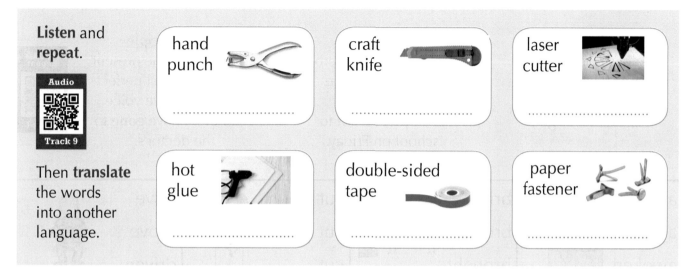

hand punch

craft knife

laser cutter

hot glue

double-sided tape

paper fastener

Practice Questions

Q1 Listen and rainbow underline. Write the sentences in your exercise book. Then use the sentence maker to write about the double-sided tape, hot glue, and paper fastener.

Audio
Track 10

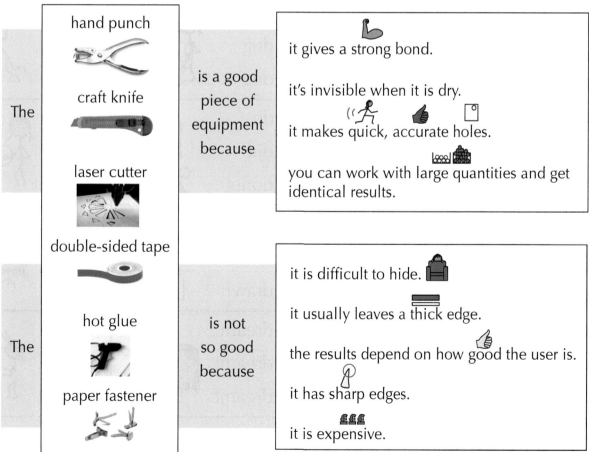

hand punch

The | craft knife | is a good piece of equipment because

laser cutter

double-sided tape

it gives a strong bond.

it's invisible when it is dry.

it makes quick, accurate holes.

you can work with large quantities and get identical results.

The | hot glue | is not so good because

paper fastener

it is difficult to hide.

it usually leaves a thick edge.

the results depend on how good the user is.

it has sharp edges.

£££
it is expensive.

"I can describe some equipment to use with paper."

Table of Irregular Verbs

Here are 100 common <u>irregular verbs</u>. You can use this list to quickly find the right <u>verb forms</u>. You can also use a <u>dictionary</u> to find out how to write a verb.

Infinitive	**Simple Past**	**Past Participle**
The basic form of the verb. You look for this in the dictionary. Example: to **go**	The form of the verb used to make the simple past. Example: I **went** to school on Friday.	Used to form the present perfect, the past perfect and the passive voice. Example: I have **gone** to the doctor's.

Listen & Repeat

Track 1

awake awoke awoken	bring brought brought	cut cut cut	drive drove driven
be was / were been	build built built	deal dealt dealt	eat ate eaten
beat beat beaten	buy bought bought	dig dug dug	fall fell fallen
begin began begun	catch caught caught	do did done	feed fed fed
bite bit bitten	choose chose chosen	draw drew drawn	feel felt felt
blow blew blown	come came come	dream dreamt dreamt	fight fought fought
break broke broken	cost cost cost	drink drank drunk	find found found

fly flew flown	have had had	lead led led	pay paid paid
forget forgot forgotten	hear heard heard	leave left left	put put put
forgive forgave forgiven	hide hid hidden	lend lent lent	quit quit quit
freeze froze frozen	hit hit hit	let let let	read read read
get got got	hold held held	lie lay lain	ride rode ridden
give gave given	hurt hurt hurt	lose lost lost	ring rang rung
go went gone	keep kept kept	make made made	rise rose risen
grow grew grown	know knew known	mean meant meant	run ran run
hang hung hung	lay laid laid	meet met met	say said said

Verb Table

see saw seen	show showed shown	stand stood stood	take took taken
seek sought sought	sing sang sung	steal stole stolen	teach taught taught
sell sold sold	sink sank sunk	stick stuck stuck	tear tore torn
send sent sent	sit sat sat	strike struck struck	tell told told
set set set	sleep slept slept	swear swore sworn	think thought thought
sew sewed sewn	slide slid slid	sweep swept swept	wear wore worn
shake shook shaken	speak spoke spoken	swell swelled swollen	weep wept wept
shine shone shone	spend spent spent	swim swam swum	win won won
shoot shot shot	spread spread spread	swing swung swung	write wrote written

Verb Table

Answers

Section 1 — Nouns

Pages 4-5 — Using the Definite Article

1. a) 8, 3, 5   b) ✓, 1, 2   c) 1, 7, ✓
   d) ✓, ✓, ✓, 7   e) ✓, 4, ✓
2. a) 4, 2, 1, 3, 6, 5 — The statue is called Christ the Redeemer.
      6, 4, 5, 1, 3, 2 — There is a statue in Rio de Janeiro.
   b) 2, 4, 1, 3, 5 — The garden is very popular.
      5, 2, 7, 3, 4, 6, 1 — Jennie Butchart designed a wonderful garden in Canada.
3. You should have written:
   There is a statue in Rio de Janeiro. The statue is called Christ the Redeemer.

   Jennie Butchart designed a wonderful garden in Canada. The garden is very popular.

Section 2 — Adjectives and Adverbs

Pages 6-7 — Comparatives and Superlatives

2. You should have underlined:
   Baking a cake is less challenging than knitting a scarf.
   Street dancing is more challenging than flying a kite.
   Goalkeeping is less rewarding than scoring.
3. Any grammatically correct superlative statements, e.g. The most rewarding hobby is knitting a scarf because it is fun to make your own clothes.
4. Any grammatically correct sentences, e.g. Playing tennis is good, playing cricket is better, but playing basketball is the best because I can see my friends.

Pages 8-9 — Adverbs of Frequency

2. You should have underlined:
   If I have a rash, I usually put cream on.
   If I have a cut, I always put on a plaster.
   If I have stomach ache, I often have a hot water bottle.
3. You should have written:
   I usually put cream on if I have a rash.
   I always put on a plaster if I have a cut.
   I often have a hot water bottle if I have stomach ache.
4. Any grammatically correct recounted story, e.g. 3 years ago, I broke my leg. I went to the hospital and visited the doctor. It took 6 weeks to get better.

Section 3 — Verbs

Pages 10-11 — Using the Simple Present

1. a) 3, 1, 6, 4, 2, 5 — It is harmful to burn fossil fuels. **(general truth)**
   b) 3, 4, 6, 2, 5, 1 — My family separates the recycling from the rubbish. **(habit)**
   c) 2, 4, 1, 6, 3, 5 — I walk to school every day. **(routine)**
   d) 6, 1, 4, 5, 2, 3 — My dad washes his car with a bucket of water. **(habit)**
   e) 2, 1, 5, 4, 3, 6 — My family eats vegetarian meals twice a week. **(routine)**

2. You should have underlined:
   Most evenings, my family eats locally grown vegetables, but yesterday evening we ate ice creams.
   On Saturdays, I go to the countryside, but last Saturday I went to a carboot sale.
   In the holidays, they plant wild flower seeds, but last holiday they planted a tree.

Pages 12-13 — Irregular Past Tense Verb Families

1. Any grammatically correct sentence pairs, e.g. Today, I catch a ball. Yesterday, I caught a ball.
2. Any grammatically correct sentences, e.g. Last Saturday, I hurt my foot.
3. set, cut, put,
   let, shut, cost,
   The missing verbs are: hurt, hit

Pages 14-15 — Common Phrasal Verbs

1. a) I **pick up** my bag from the floor.
   b) I **go back** to get my coat.
   c) We **line up** in the queue.
   d) We **put on** our shoes.
2. Any grammatically correct sentences, e.g. My cousin looks up to his dad because he is kind.
3. Any grammatically correct rewritten sentences, e.g. My cousin looked up to his dad when he was kind last weekend.

Section 4 — Prepositions

Pages 16-17 — Prepositions in Time Phrases: In

2. Any grammatically correct sentences, e.g. In my country, it is always cold in autumn but in the UK, it is sometimes warm in autumn.
3. a) *eighteen thirty-six*
   b) nineteen fourty-seven
   c) seventeen sixty-nine
   d) two thousand and eleven
   e) nineteen twelve
   f) two thousand and eighteen
   g) two thousand
   h) two thousand and seven

Pages 18-19 — Prepositions in Time Phrases: On

1. a) English, science and computing
   b) Wednesday
2. Any grammatically correct questions and answers, e.g. When does Maria need to remember her geography books? Maria needs to remember her geography books on Tuesdays.

Section 5 — Reading Comprehension

Pages 20-21 — Retrieval and Inference

1   participate — to take part or join in
community — a group of people with something in common
service — a religious meeting
adult — a grown-up
ceremony — a special religious meeting
set an example — show others the right thing to do

2

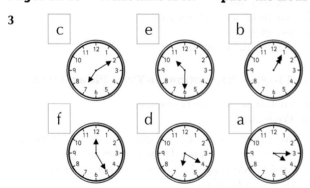

Bar Mitzvah

When a Jewish boy is around 13 years old, he has his Bar Mitzvah ceremony. It is a very important moment in his life. After his Bar Mitzvah ceremony, the Jewish community sees him as an adult.

He participates in the services at the synagogue, reads from the Torah and has to set a good example to other boys.

At a similar age, some Jewish girls also have a coming-of-age ceremony called a Bat Mitzvah.

3   You should have underlined:
'around 13 years old', 'the Jewish community sees him as an adult', 'the Torah', 'the synagogue', 'some Jewish girls also have a coming-of-age ceremony', 'At a similar age'

4   Any sensible full-sentence answers, e.g.
2) It is an important moment in a Jewish boy's life because after his Bar Mitzvah ceremony, the Jewish community sees him as an adult.
3) The Jewish holy book is called the Torah.
4) Jews hold their religious services in a synagogue.
5) No, only some Jewish girls have a coming-of-age ceremony.
6) Girls are around 13 when they have their Bat Mitzvah.

Section 6 — Maths Language

Pages 22-23 — What time is it? — 'past' the Hour

3   c   e   b
f   d   a

4   Ali wakes up at 8 o'clock.
Ali eats lunch at 1 o'clock.
Ali goes to bed at half past 9.

Section 7 — Nouns

Pages 24-25 — Concrete, Abstract and Collective Nouns

1   Proper nouns — London, Amir,
London Underground, Billingsgate Market,
Covent Garden Market, Borough Market
Concrete nouns — trip, cousin, traffic jams, markets,
Traders, fish, antiques, foods
Abstract nouns — happiness, friendship, frustration,
freedom, knowledge, interest

2   Any grammatically correct sentences,
e.g. To finish a project, you need **patience**.

3

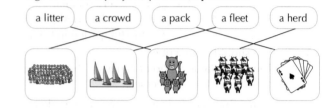

Section 8 — Adjectives and Adverbs

Pages 26-27 — Adjectives Ending in '-ed' and 'ing'

1   You should have underlined:
I am amazed by your dribbling skills.
I am bored of defending all the time.
I am interested in learning new skills.

2   Any grammatically correct sentences,
e.g. I am frightened of missing a penalty.

3   Any grammatically correct rewritten sentences,
e.g. Missing a penalty is frightening.

4   Any grammatically correct sentences,
e.g. I am encouraged by my progress.

5   Any grammatically correct sentences,
e.g. My favourite hobby is karate because it is exciting.

Pages 28-29 — Adverbials of Place and Time

1 **a)**   6, 3, 1, 5, 2, 4 — The policeman arrested three robbers in an alleyway.
b)   2, 5, 4, 1, 6, 3 — The manager paid the bills at the bank.

2   Any grammatically correct sentences,
e.g. The superhero rescued a child at the beach a month ago.

Section 9 — Verbs

Pages 30-31 — The Past Participle

1

Present	Simple Past	Past Participle
fly	flew	*flown*
nibble	nibbled	nibbled
go	*went*	gone
hatch	hatched	*hatched*
eat	ate	eaten

3   The worm has **gone** underground.
A bee has **flown** into the hive with its nectar.
The spider has **eaten** the fly.
The beetle has **hatched** from a tiny egg.

4   The past participles are: broken, annoyed

I was **annoyed** by the buzzing mosquito.
The beetle had a **broken** wing.

Pages 32-33 — The Present Perfect

1   Any grammatically correct questions and answers,
      e.g. Have you ever broken your leg?
            No, I haven't broken my leg.

2   Any grammatically correct answers,
      e.g. Have you ever had chickenpox?
            Taku has had chickenpox.

Pages 34-35 — The Past Perfect

1   7, 3, 1, 6, 4, 2, 5

      You should have written:
      Yesterday, I decided to bake a chocolate cake for my
      sister. <u>She had eaten</u> all the chocolate, so I went to
      the supermarket.
      <u>I hadn't written</u> a list. When I got to the till, I realised
      that <u>I'd forgotten</u> the chocolate, so I had to go back to
      get it.
      Back home, I put the mixture in the oven after
      <u>I had mixed</u> it.
      Three hours later, I took my cake out of the oven.
      <u>I had forgotten</u> to set the timer.
      It was black and <u>it hadn't risen</u> because <u>I hadn't added</u>
      the eggs.
      What's more, <u>it had stuck</u> to the tin.
      I wished that <u>I had bought</u> a cake instead.

2   a) 3, 5, *1*, 2, 6, 4, 7 — <u>I had just whipped</u> the cream
                        when my sister arrived home.
      b) 3, 2, 6, 1, 4, 5, 7 — The cake <u>had just cooled</u> enough,
                        so I quickly covered it with the
                        cream.
      c) 6, 2, 4, 1, 3, 5, 7 — She said that it looked delicious
                        but she <u>had just eaten</u> lunch.

3   Any sensible ending to the story that uses the past
      perfect, e.g. **I had just cut** her a slice, so I wrapped
      it up for her.

Pages 36-37 — The Passive Voice

1   a) 7, 2, 6, *1*, 3, 5, 4
      b) 2, 5, 4, 3, 7, 1, 6
      c) 6, 1, 8, 2, 5, 7, 3, 4

2   a) Mongolian horses <u>are raced</u> at the Naadam festival.
      b) Paint <u>is thrown</u> during Holi in India.
      c) Fancy costumes <u>are worn</u> for Carnival in Brazil.

3   b) *At the Lantern Festival,* paper lanterns are lit by
         Taiwanese people.
      c) *During Day of the Dead,* prayers for the dead are said
         by Mexican people.
      d) *At Songkran,* water is thrown by Thai people.

Section 10 — Prepositions

Pages 38-39 — Using 'On', 'In' and 'At'

1   Any grammatically correct story, e.g.
      a) Last week, the postman was delivering a parcel **in**
         Pakistan.
      b) He prefers to travel **on** a boat
      c) because he likes listening to rock music **on** his radio.
      d) He took a wrong turn and went up a street **on** the left
      e) and by magic ended up **in** Timbuktu.

3   Any grammatically correct sentences,
      e.g. I saw a dog at the side of the football pitch.

Pages 40-41 — Directions

2   Any grammatically correct dialogues, e.g.
      Excuse me? Can you tell me the way to the **library**,
      please? / Go straight ahead. Take the **second** road on
      the **right**. It will be on your **right** and **opposite** the
      river. / Thank you very much. Have a good day.

      Excuse me? Can you tell me the way to the **museum**,
      please? / Continue along the street. Go over the
      bridge and into the square. It will be on your **left** and
      across from the **church**. / Thank you very much. Have
      a good day.

Section 11 — Reading Comprehension

Pages 42-43 — Mary Seacole

2   5 *Caribbean, who...*   4 *medicines and...*
      8 *started her...*   10 *they didn't...*
      6 *in 1853...*   11 *was very...*
      2 *a determined...*   7 *friends, but...*
      3 *was Jamaican...*   1 *Mary Seacole...*
      9 *her. She...*

3   1) *determined and caring*
      2) good hygiene, herbal medicines and nursing skills
      3) because they were her friends
      4) the British government didn't want her help
      5) The British Hotel
      6) Florence Nightingale
      7) England

4   taught   started
      wanted   moved

5   1) Mary Seacole was determined and caring.
      2) Her mother taught her about good hygiene, herbal
         medicines and nursing skills.
      3) Mary wanted to help the soldiers because they
         were her friends.
      4) Mary started her own hospital because the British
         government didn't want her help.
      5) Mary's hospital was called The British Hotel.
      6) The famous British nurse that Mary met was called
         Florence Nightingale.
      7) Mary moved to England in 1856.

Section 12 — Maths Language

Pages 44-45 — Telling the Time — 'to' the Hour

2
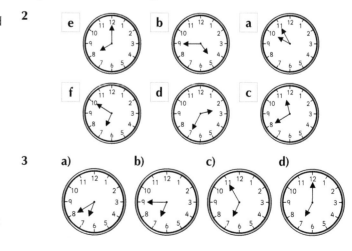

3   a)   b)   c)   d)

4   In 2020, Eid al-Fitr was **in** May, but it falls **in** different months and **in** different seasons because it is around 11 days earlier each year.
For most Christians, Christmas is **on** 25th December. Some begin their celebrations **at** midnight, with a Midnight Mass. However, many celebrate **on** 6th January instead.
Time is spent with family, special meals are eaten, smart clothes are worn and gifts are given both **at** Eid and **at** Christmas.

Section 13 — Using a Dictionary

Pages 46-47 — Using a Dictionary

1 **a)** 3, 5, 1, 4, 2
    b) 3, 1, 4, 2, 5
2   delicatessen — *You can buy cold foods, usually cheese and meat.*
hardware shop — *You can buy tools.*
butcher's — *You can buy meat.*
pharmacy — *You can buy medicine.*
charity shop — *You can buy used items like clothes.*
3   nouns — purchase, return, basket, till, trolley, cash
adjectives — busy, friendly, convenient
verbs — purchase, enquire, return, cash
adverbs — loudly, quickly, happily
4   Any grammatically correct sentences,
e.g. I **return** the **trolley quickly.**

Section 14 — More Subject Language

Page 48 — Chemistry — The Periodic Table

3 **a)** metal   **b)** gas   **c)** element   **d)** atom

Page 49 — Physics — Electricity

1
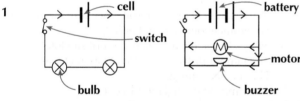
2   Any grammatically correct sentences, e.g. The bulbs will shine more brightly when there are more cells.

3   Any grammatically correct sentences, e.g. The buzzer will buzz more loudly when there are more cells.

Page 50 — Biology — Human Organs

1   You should have underlined:
The lungs help us breathe and they bring oxygen into our body.
The brain helps us think, have emotions and control the other organs.
The heart helps all the other organs to work by pumping blood everywhere. You can feel it working when you touch your chest.

The stomach helps us digest the food we eat before it goes to the intestine.
The kidneys help us keep the body and the blood clean from toxins (bad stuff).
The skin helps us maintain our body temperature. It covers the whole body.

Page 51 — Geography — World Climate Zones

1   You should have underlined:
In a polar climate it is very cold all year.
A Mediterranean climate has hot summers and mild winters.
A temperate climate has mild summers and cold winters.

Any grammatically correct sentences, e.g.
In an arid climate it is dry and hot all year.
In a tropical climate it is hot and wet all year.
In a mountain climate it is usually cold with weather that changes quickly.

2 **a)** tropical **b)** temperate **c)** Mediterranean **d)** arid

Page 52 — History — WWII Timeline

1 **a)** 3, 1, 5, 2, 6, 4 — Germany invaded Poland which began WWII.
    b) 3, 2, 5, 1, 6, 4 — Germany took control of many countries including Denmark and France.
    c) 3, 4, 2, 5, 1, 6 — Germany, Italy and Japan signed a treaty to work together.
    d) 4, 2, 3, 5, 1 — Japan attacked Pearl Harbour in the United States.
    e) 5, 1, 2, 4, 3 — Italy surrendered but Mussolini escaped capture.
    f) 3, 5, 4, 6, 2, 1 — Germany finally surrendered after Hitler's suicide.
    g) 3, 2, 5, 1, 6, 4 — The U.S. dropped two atomic bombs on Japan.
    h) 5, 4, 1, 2, 3 — Japan surrendered which ended WWII.

2   Any grammatically correct sentences that include the correct preposition and date, e.g.
Between April and June 1940, Germany took control of many countries including Denmark and France.

Page 53 — D&T — Working with Paper

1   You should have underlined:
The hand punch is a good piece of equipment because it makes quick, accurate holes.
The craft knife is not so good because the results depend on how good the user is.
The laser cutter is a good piece of equipment because you can work with large quantities and get identical results.

Any grammatically correct sentences, e.g.
The double-sided tape is a good piece of equipment because it gives a strong bond.
The hot glue is not so good because it usually leaves a thick edge.

AIFR331